Foreword

The project leading to this report is part of a CIRIA programme 'Concrete Techniques - Site Operations', and was carried out under contract by Dr T A Harrison.

Steering Group

The project was carried out and the report prepared under the guidance of the following Steering Group:

Mr R A McClelland [Chairman]	– Alfred McAlpine Construction Ltd.
Dr P Bamforth	– Taywood Engineering Ltd.
Mr R Cather	– Arup Research & Development
Mr B Cowling	– Appleby Group
Mr S Crompton	– Ready Mixed Concrete (UK) Ltd.
Dr B Marsh	– Building Research Establishment
Mr G G T Masterton	– Babtie Shaw & Morton
Mr A McGibney	– Civil and Marine Slag Cement Ltd
Dr J B Newman	– Imperial College of Science, Technology and Medicine
Mr A J Nicklinson	– Trafalgar House Construction (Major Projects) Ltd.
Mr P L Owens	– Quality Ash Association
Mr R Roberts	– Concrete Advisory Service
Mr P Titman	– Edmund Nuttall
Mr C Turton	– Design Group Partnership
Dr B W Staynes	– CIRIA Research Manager

Funding

The project was funded by the Department of the Environment and CIRIA.

Contents

List of Figures 6
List of Tables 7
Notation 8
Abbreviations 9

1 INTRODUCTION 10

2 DEFINITIONS OF CONCRETE STRENGTH 11

3 STRIKING CRITERIA 15
3.1 Structural cracking and collapse 15
3.2 Deflection 18
3.3 Freeze/thaw damage 19
3.4 Mechanical damage to the concrete by the removal of formwork 19
3.5 Further mechanical damage 20
3.6 Moisture loss 21
3.7 Colour variation 21
3.8 Durability 21
3.9 Thermal cracking and shock 21
3.10 Site requirements 22
3.11 Summary of methods of determining the concrete strength required for striking 22
3.11.1 Soffit formwork using Sadgrove's relationship 22
3.11.2 Soffit formwork by analysis of the actual section 22
3.11.3 Vertical formwork 22

4 PREDICTING THE STRENGTH OF CONCRETE 24
4.1 Introduction 24
4.2 Maturity 24
4.3 Predictive methods 27
4.4 Calculation of the heat generated 29
4.5 Prediction of formwork striking times using job-specific data 33
4.6 Prediction of formwork striking times using non job-specific data 34
4.7 Tables of formwork striking times 35

5 REDUCTION OF FORMWORK STRIKING TIMES 40

6 METHODS OF DETERMINING STRIKING TIMES 43
6.1 Introduction 43
6.2 Cubes cured alongside 43
6.3 Temperature-matched cubes 44
6.4 Penetration tests 44
6.5 Pull-out tests 44
6.6 Break-off tests 47
6.7 Maturity measurements 49

7 CONCLUSIONS 51

REFERENCES 52

APPENDIX A: SELECTION OF CONCRETE STRENGTH REQUIRED TO WITHSTAND A KNOWN WIND LOADING ON A REINFORCED CONCRETE WALL OR COLUMN 59
A.1 Introduction 59
A.2 Derivation of charts 61
A.2.1 Crushing of the concrete 61
A.2.2 Check on anchorage bond failure 63
A.2.3 Derivation of figures 63

APPENDIX B: THE APPLICATION OF THE SADGROVE EQUATION TO CEMENTS CONTAINING GGBS 64

APPENDIX C: THE APPLICATION OF THE SADGROVE EQUATION TO CEMENTS CONTAINING PFA 68

APPENDIX D: EXAMPLE OF A HAND CALCULATION OF MATURITY USING THE SADGROVE EQUATION 71

FIGURES

Figure 2.1 *Relationship between concrete strengths* 12
Figure 2.2 *Relationship between instrument reading and the mean strength of cubes from Equation [2.1]* 13
Figure 3.1 *Probability of striking formwork without mechanical damage to the concrete surface* 20
Figure 4.1 *Typical envelope of strength for PC-42.5 concretes* 25
Figure 4.2 *Strength gain for a specific PC-42.5 concrete* 25
Figure 4.3 *A typical adiabatic calorimeter* 29
Figure 4.4 *Adiabatic temperature rise* 30
Figure 4.5 *Heat per kg cement against maturity* 31
Figure 4.6 *Isothermal conduction calorimeter* 32
Figure 4.7 *Rates of heat evolution from cement under isothermal conditions* 32
Figure 4.8 *An example of measured and predicted temperatures using Concrete Hardening Control System taken from reference 33* 33
Figure 4.9 *Measured and predicted temperatures using the BCA system for a UK construction* 34
Figure 5.1 *Typical strength gain of concretes of equal workability but different grades* 41
Figure 5.2 *Strength gain at 20°C of high and medium workability PC-42.5 concretes* 41
Figure 5.3 *Effect of formwork type on the temperature and equivalent age at the concrete surface* 42
Figure 6.1 *Temperature-matched curing* 45
Figure 6.2 *Windsor Probe penetration test* 46
Figure 6.3 *The principle of the LOK test* 47
Figure 6.4 *The LOK test equipment* 47
Figure 6.5 *The break-off test* 48
Figure 6.6 *A maturity meter (photograph by courtesy of Wexham Developments Ltd.)* 49
Figure 6.7 *The COMA maturity probe* 50
Figure A.1 *Cube strength required to withstand wind speeds up to 10 m/s (36 km/h)* 59

Figure A.2 *Cube strength required to withstand wind speeds up to 15 m/s (54 km/h)* 60
Figure A.3 *Cube strength required to withstand wind speeds up to 20 m/s (72 km/h)* 60
Figure A.4 *Wind loads on walls* 61
Figure B.1 *Mix A with 40% ggbs 1* 64
Figure B.2 *Mix A with 40% ggbs 2* 64
Figure B.3 *Mix B with 40% ggbs 1* 65
Figure B.4 *Mix B with 40% ggbs 2* 65
Figure B.5 *Mix A with 70% ggbs 1* 66
Figure B.6 *Mix A with 70% ggbs 2* 66
Figure B.7 *Mix B with 70% ggbs 1* 67
Figure B.8 *Mix B with 70% ggbs 2* 67
Figure C.1 *Mix M2* 68
Figure C.2 *Mix M3* 69
Figure C.3 *Mix M4* 69
Figure C.4 *Mix M5* 70

TABLES

Table 3.1 *Ultimate local bond stresses (N/mm²)* 17
Table 4.1 *Comparison of "k" values for Portland cement-42.5 and 52.5 concretes, obtained from equations [4.2] and [4.3]* 26
Table 4.2 *Specific heats of concrete and its components* 28
Table 4.3 *Coefficient of thermal transmittance of form face and insulating materials* 29
Table 4.4 *Minimum rates of strength development for the application of the PC-42.5 striking times* 35
Table 4.5 *Minimum rates of strength development for the application of the PC-52.5 striking times* 36
Table 4.6 *Minimum striking times (days) for slab and beam soffits with an uninsulated top surface* 37
Table 4.7 *Minimum striking times (days) for slab and beam soffits with 18mm plywood formwork and a 20mm enclosed air gap on the top surface* 38
Table 4.8 *Minimum striking times (days) for slab and beam soffits with 25mm expanded polystyrene on all surfaces* 39

Notation

Symbols used in this Report are mainly from BS 8110 and CP 3: Chapter V: Part 2. To align with common usage in the construction industry, temperature differences have been given the unit "°C" and not the numerically equal unit "K".

Symbol	Units	
A_s	mm^2	Area of tension steel per metre run of wall
b	mm	Width of section
C	kg/m^3	Cement content
C_f	-	Effective force coefficient
c	kJ/kg°C	Specific heat of concrete
d	mm	Effective depth
E	kJ/mol	Activation energy obtained experimentally
D_c	kg/m^3	Density of concrete
f_{ba}	N/mm^2	Anchorage bond stress
f_{cu}	N/mm^2	Characteristic concrete cube strength
f_1	N/mm^2	Characteristic concrete cube strength required to withstand direct stress
f_2	N/mm^2	Characteristic concrete cube strength required to withstand bending stress
f_y	N/mm^2	Characteristic strength of reinforcement
$H_{g\,max}$	-	Maximum degree of hydration
h	mm	Overall depth of section in plane of bending
k	-	Maturity function
L	m	Height of lift
M	h	Equivalent age at 20°C
M_u	N.mm	Ultimate resistance moment
M_w	N.mm	Moment resulting from wind load per metre width of wall
Q	kJ/kg	Heat evolved at maturity M
Q_c	kJ/kg	Total heat evolved when $M \rightarrow \infty$
q	N/mm^2	Wind load per unit area
R	-	Molar gas constant
s_b	mm	Spacing of bars
t	h	Selected time
t_d	h	Dormant period
t_c	h	Time constant
V	kN	Shear force from dead and construction loads
V_s	m/s	Maximum wind speed
W	kJ/kg	Theoretical full heat generation (ie 100% hydration)
γ_{mc}	-	Partial safety factor for concrete at early age
Δt	-	Time increment
$\Delta\theta$	°C	Increase in temperature at time t
$\Delta\theta_{max}$	°C	Maximum increase of temperature under adiabatic conditions
τ_c	h	Constant
ϕ	mm	Effective diameter of reinforcement
θ	°C	Mean concrete temperature

Abbreviations

ggbs	Ground granulated blastfurnace slag
PC-42.5 or 52.5	Portland cement to BS12:1991 of cement strength class 42.5 or 52.5. (The ENV197: Part 1 equivalents are CEM 1-42.5 or 52.5 cements)
pfa	Pulverised-fuel ash to BS3892
SRPC-42.5	Sulphate-resisting Portland cement to BS4027:1991 of cement strength class 42.5

1 Introduction

Since the beginning of concrete construction, the decision to remove formwork and allow the structure to support itself has been a matter for judgement between the needs for speed of construction and for avoidance of collapse or damage. Normally, striking times have been conservative, but failures have nevertheless occurred[1]. Based on methods and data developed in a series of research programmes[2-8], CIRIA has published three reports on formwork striking. These were *Formwork striking time - methods of assessment*[9] which was first published in 1977 with a revised edition in 1987, *Striking times of formwork-curing periods to achieve given strengths*[10] and its replacement *Tables of minimum striking times for soffit and vertical formwork*[11]. This report incorporates these previous reports and supersedes them. In addition, it describes the predictive methods for estimating formwork striking times.

The subjects of backpropping, i.e. the means of distributing construction loads through more than one level, and repropping, i.e. replacing some of the original supports in a sequence to avoid damage to the young concrete, are not covered in this report as they are adequately covered in *Formwork: A guide to good practice*[12].

The wider appreciation of time-related costs has resulted in commercial pressure to build quickly. An important facet of rapid construction is an understanding of the factors governing formwork striking times (and thereby the ability to minimise them without prejudicing safety). This report describes methods for predicting and assessing formwork striking times which are suitable for use with rapid construction.

The decision to authorise the removal of formwork requires two steps. Firstly the criterion that controls the striking time has to be identified and in most cases, expressed as a strength requirement from cubes of equal maturity to the structure. These criteria are described in Section 3. The second step is to determine when this strength has been achieved. Methods of determining the striking time are reviewed in Sections 6 and 4.7.

When planning the sequence of construction, it is necessary to estimate the formwork striking times. Reliable estimates of the striking times can have a significant impact on time and costs. For example, it may be possible to save one set of forms. Section 4 gives a synopsis of the computer-based techniques used for predicting the in-situ strength of concrete and hence the formwork striking times.

However, for a better understanding of this report, certain concepts relating to concrete strength are described in the following section. The concept of maturity is widely used in this report to relate the development of concrete strength to that obtained at 20°C. Maturity is described in Section 4.2.

2 Definitions of concrete strength

The characteristic cube strength of concrete is defined statistically as the strength below which no more than 5% of test cubes would be expected to fall. The term is normally applied to 28-day concrete made, cured and tested in accordance with BS 1881[13], but can also be applied to concrete of any maturity. The grade of concrete and the specified 28-day characteristic strength (abbreviated to specified strength) are terms used to describe the required characteristic strength of cubes after 28 days' curing in accordance with BS 1881. This specified strength, which relates to test cubes and not to the concrete within the structure, is that normally used for structural design calculations.

The difference between the mean cube strength and the characteristic strength is called 'the margin'.

An analysis of a section to determine the formwork striking time gives the characteristic strength required from cubes of equal maturity to the structure and from this an estimate of an adequate mean strength is made. Hence:

Required mean strength of cubes
= Characteristic strength of cubes + a margin [2.1]

When formwork striking times are to be assessed, the data on which the decision is made are so few that it is not appropriate to use statistics to determine the margin. Therefore the margin can be expressed either as a constant value or as a percentage of the characteristic strength. Because the characteristic strength required for soffit striking can range from 5 to 30 N/mm^2, expressing the margin as a percentage gives a constant factor of safety. For striking of formwork, a 25% margin is recommended. Then:

Required mean strength of cubes
= 1.25 × [characteristic strength of cubes] [2.2]

So far, the discussion has been limited to cubes, but the strength of the test specimens has to be related to the in-situ strength.

The concept of an in-situ cube strength is used throughout this Report. This is a theoretical concept, because it is not possible to directly measure the cube strength within an element, even if cubes are cut from the element. The in-situ cube strength is the crushing strength a cube has if the state of the concrete within the cube is identical to that within the element. This is not the same as the strength of a cube of equal maturity, because there are inevitable differences in compaction and moisture condition between the element and a test cube.

BS 8110[14] introduces a partial safety factor for materials, γ_m, to take into account possible differences between the strength of the material in the actual structure and the characteristic strength derived from test specimens. This factor has also been defined[15] as the characteristic strength divided by the design strength, or as the ratio of the 28-day characteristic strength to the characteristic in-situ cube strength. For early-age work, these definitions cannot sensibly be used, because the 28-day characteristic strength is fixed while the in-situ characteristic strength is changing significantly as the section changes in maturity. For example, ignoring all differences except age, a Grade 30 concrete cured at 20°C could require a partial factor of safety at 1, 3 and 7 days of 11.5, 2.5 and 1.6, respectively. With early-age work, the philosophical requirements of a safety factor to allow for differences in workmanship and curing between the site-placed concrete and the test specimens, and for strength variations within the structure, remain the same, but maturity is specifically taken into account and therefore should be eliminated from the safety factor. Taking the partial safety factor as a ratio between a characteristic strength of test cubes and the in-situ cube strength at the same maturity fulfils these requirements, and it enables the factor to be taken as a constant. To differentiate this partial factor of safety from γ_m, it is referred to as γ_{mc}. Then:

Characteristic strength of cubes at any maturity
= γ_{mc} × characteristic in-situ cube strength at the same maturity [2.3]

In considering soffit striking, Sadgrove[5] assumes γ_{mc} to be 1.5, and he expresses this relationship in terms of the characteristic strength of cubes of equal maturity to the in-situ concrete (i.e. the left-hand term of Equation [2.3]).

Putting $\gamma_{mc} = 1.5$

and allowing for the margin by substituting into Equations [2.2] and [2.3]

Required mean strength of cubes
= 1.88 × [characteristic in-situ cube strength] [2.4]

If the characteristic in-situ cube strength is assumed to be the stress to which the concrete is subjected, this expression is in good agreement with the phrase in clause 6.9.3.2 of BS 8110 which states that the concrete should have a mean strength of 10 N/mm^2, or twice the stress to which it is subjected, whichever is the greater. Figure 2.1 shows graphically the relationship between the various strengths.

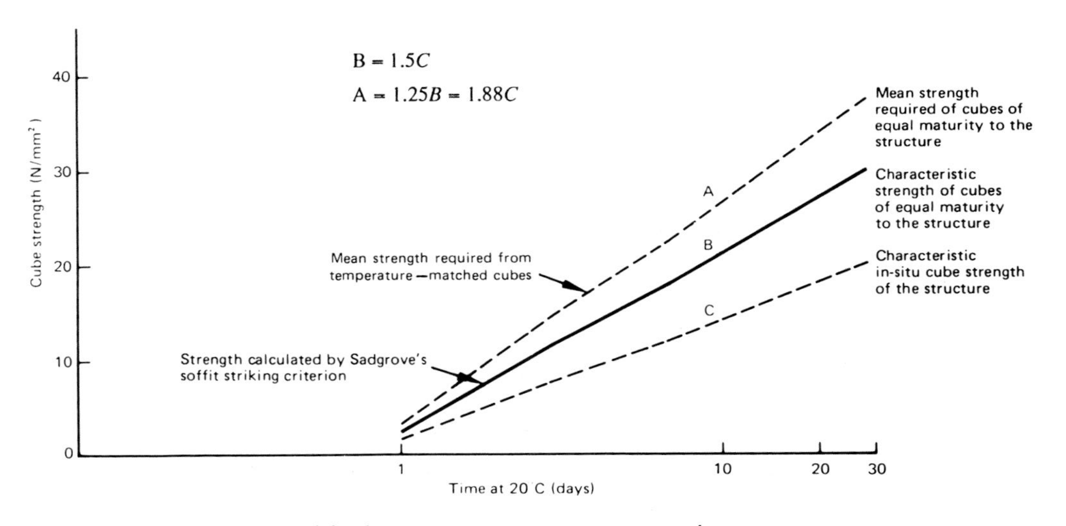

Figure 2.1 *Relationship between concrete strengths*

Most striking time tests which are directly carried out on the structure require an additional factor to ensure that a safe relationship between instrument reading and cube strength is used. There are at least two ways of achieving this. One method is to calculate the required mean cube strength from Equation [2.1], then convert to instrument reading, using the experimentally established 90% confidence limit (see Figure 2.2). This gives a 95% probability that the cube strength is greater than assumed.

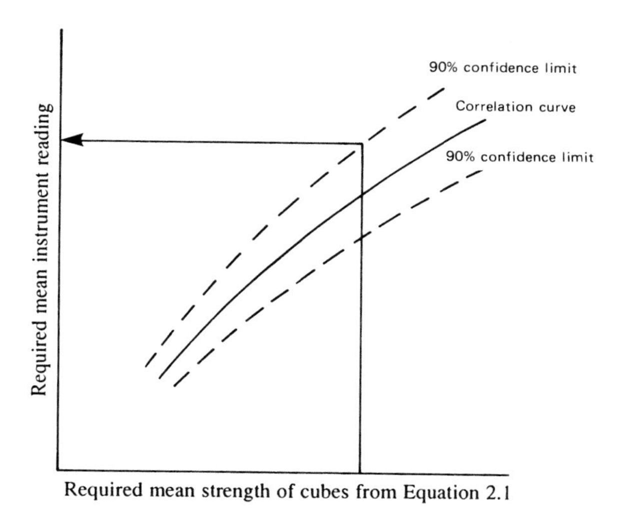

Figure 2.2 *Relationship between instrument reading and the mean strength of cubes from Equation [2.1]*

An alternative method may be used when more than, say, five instrument readings are taken on a section. The mean and standard deviation of the instrument readings are calculated. The characteristic instrument reading is then calculated using:

Characteristic instrument reading

$$= Mean\ instrument\ reading - \frac{t_{0.05}\ standard\ deviation}{\sqrt{n}} \quad [2.5]$$

where n is the number of instrument readings

and $t_{0.05}$ = 2.132 when n = 5
= 2.015 when n = 6
= 1.943 when n = 7
= 1.895 when n = 8
= 1.860 when n = 9
= 1.833 when n = 10
= 1.812 when n = 11
= 1.796 when n = 12

The characteristic instrument reading is then converted to cube strength using the correlation curve. This method takes into account only testing error, not model error, and it should therefore only be used when the model error is small. Model error is the error in the assumed relationship between the instrument reading and the cube strength.

In theory, if the structure is directly tested[16], a lower in-situ strength is acceptable[17]. The strength can be up to $1.2/\gamma_{mc}$ times less than tests on cubes of equal maturity to the structure. In practice, the partial factor of safety for materials takes into account factors which are not material related (e.g. dimensional errors), and therefore careful consideration should be given before working to this degree of refinement.

3 Striking criteria

When formwork is removed from in-situ concrete, a number of potential problems need to be avoided, the most serious being the collapse of the structure. If, in removing the formwork, a large part of the concrete surface is removed, the durability of the structure could be impaired by the reduction of the cover to reinforcement, and the appearance of the structure might not be acceptable. The ultimate strength of the concrete may be considerably reduced if it is frozen before it has reached an in-situ strength of 2 N/mm^2.

The factors to be considered in setting the criteria for formwork striking are:

- collapse
- deflection
- freeze/thaw damage
- mechanical damage to the concrete by the removal of formwork
- further mechanical damage (due to site operations)
- moisture loss
- colour variation
- durability
- thermal cracking and shock
- site requirements

The research into each aspect of striking formwork and the development of the striking criteria are discussed in this section. The minimum striking time is generally calculated by determining the cube strength required to satisfy all the criteria.

A summary of how to determine the concrete strength required for striking is given in Section 3.11.

3.1 STRUCTURAL CRACKING AND COLLAPSE

Collapse is the most serious limit state. Removal of formwork before the concrete has achieved the necessary strength has resulted in catastrophic failure with loss of life.

The relationship between the in-situ cube strength and the applied load was studied by Sadgrove[4,5], who first verified that, for concrete at early age, the percentage gain of compressive strength was lower than the gain of bond strength and about equal to the gain of tensile strength.

An experimental check on what was then the draft form of CP 110 (now BS 8110[14]) showed that calculated resistance moments gave safe estimates for beams at early age. Sadgrove then showed that for a balanced or over-reinforced beam, the resistance moment was directly proportional to compressive strength up to the specified concrete strength. Because the gain of bond strength, as a percentage of its 28-day value, is more rapid than the percentage gain of compressive strength[4], bond is not a limiting criterion with such sections. Until the specified concrete strength is attained, these sections fail by the concrete crushing. With under-reinforced sections, at early ages, the percentage of the designed resistance moment attained is higher than that of a balanced section, and therefore bond could become the limiting criterion. To avoid the possibility of bond failure, Sadgrove based his relationship between cube strength and the safe applied load on a balanced section. This relationship is conservative for under-reinforced sections[4].

An experiment was devised to check that the early loading of a member did not affect its design ultimate moment. Pairs of beams were cast, then, at various ages, one was tested to destruction and the other loaded with a percentage of the measured early-age ultimate moment. The results showed that loading beams up to 87% of their early-age ultimate moment did not significantly affect their design ultimate moment.

The conclusion from this work was that a concrete member can safely support a load which bears the same ratio to its designed working load as the characteristic strength of cubes of equal maturity as the in-situ concrete bears to its specified 28-day characteristic strength. See 3.11.1 for a stage by stage example of this calculation.

Alternatively, the characteristic strength required from cubes of equal maturity as the in-situ concrete can be obtained from an analysis of the as-cast section. It is important that the approach to the analysis is the same as that used for the original design. For example, if the structure was designed using plastic analysis and then the formwork striking times were to be based on an elastic analysis using "twice the (extreme fibre) stress", it might be concluded that the forms could never be removed! This was not the intention of the phrase "twice the stress" in BS8110.

In a section analysis to obtain the characteristic strength needed before the forms can be removed, it is reasonable to modify the partial safety factors for loading. No clear guidance is published, but formwork design[12] is based on conservative estimates of loads and partial safety factors for loading of 1.0. However, it should be noted that formwork design tends to be very conservative. Structural design can be more sophisticated and consequently less conservative and therefore it is prudent to apply partial safety factors greater than 1.0, say 1.2 for both dead and construction loads. It should be noted that when the Sadgrove relationship is used (see 3.11.1), the partial safety factors are taken as 1.0 for both the load at striking and the designed working load. The dead load is based on the loads at the time of formwork striking, e.g. finishes are not normally included, and the estimate of the construction loads should be realistic. If large construction loads are to be applied shortly after formwork striking, repropping is almost certainly going to be required.

In under-reinforced sections, moment resistance develops more rapidly than cube strength[5]. Collapse by exceeding the ultimate moment can be prevented if:

Mean strength of cubes of equal
maturity to the in-situ concrete $\geq 1.25 \times M/0.15\ bd^2$ [3.1]

where M = maximum moment produced by the factored self-weight and construction loads

b = width of section

d = effective depth of tension reinforcement

The shear and torsion capacities can be checked by assuming that they develop proportionally at the same rate as cube strength[18]

$$\text{i.e.}\quad \frac{\textit{Shear capacity at time t}}{\textit{Ultimate shear capacity}} \geq \frac{\textit{Cube strength at time t}}{\textit{Grade of concrete}} \qquad [3.2]$$

The development of punching shear with time has not been investigated, and Wilson[18] recommends particular caution. He suggests that punching shear is assumed to develop in proportion to the development of cube strength.

Serviceability checks on bond stress are not included in BS 8110, but they can be the critical design criterion for formwork striking, particularly adjacent to sections not yet cast[19]. Wilson[18] also draws attention to the high bond slip before bond failure with deformed bars. According to Sadgrove[4], at early ages the bond strength is more fully developed than the cube strength in comparison with their 28-day values. A conservative assumption is to assume that local bond strength develops at the same rate as cube strength.

The mean cube strength to prevent local bond failure needs to be

$$1.25 \times \frac{V}{\Sigma u_s \times d} \times \frac{\textit{Grade of concrete}}{\textit{Ultimate local bond stress}} \qquad [3.3]$$

where V = shear force from dead and construction loads
Σu_s = the sum of the effective perimeters of the tension reinforcement
d = effective depth of section

The ultimate local bond stresses are given in Table 3.1.

Table 3.1 *Ultimate local bond stresses (N/mm²)*

Bar type	**Concrete Grade**			
	20	**25**	**30**	**40 or more**
Plain	1.7	2.0	2.2	2.7
Type 1 (square twisted)	2.1	2.5	2.8	3.4
Type 2 (ribbed)	2.5	3.0	3.4	4.1

after CP 110: Part 1: 1972

Note: Only valid for bars parallel to compression face.

The limit state of collapse does not only apply to beams and slabs. Wind loading on walls and columns can be the limiting striking time criterion. For example, some concrete walls built in the coastal area of Holland were required to have an in-situ cube strength of 3.5 N/mm^2 before support could be removed although the freeze/thaw and mechanical damage criteria require an in-situ cube strength of only 2 N/mm^2. The form design was such that adequate support against wind loading was obtained by striking one side of the formwork the following morning and leaving the other form face in contact with the concrete until the required strength was reached. Repropping walls is an alternative solution where wind loading is critical. A simple method for determining the concrete strength required to withstand wind loads is given in Appendix A.

Some soffit formwork is constructed with 'quickstrip' systems where the soffit formwork can be removed without disturbing the props. The props modify the distribution of load and the structure does not act as in its designed state. The critical condition limiting the time of striking is likely to be at the prop heads, where punching shear acts in combination with the tensile forces created by the hogging moment. At this stage, no positive recommendations can be made.

The subject of backpropping and repropping in multi-storey buildings has been examined in a number of publications[12,20-26].

3.2 DEFLECTION

Sadgrove[5] looked at the problem of the deflection under sustained early loading of balanced section beams having span/depth ratios of under 6 and over 6. This gave limit states of collapse and deflection, respectively. In the first case, he calculated the effect of applying a moment at an early age equal to two-thirds of the resistance moment at that age prior to application of full working moment at 28 days. The total deflections were thereby increased by up to 18%. However, in the same publication, it was experimentally demonstrated that the method of calculating creep deflection for beams loaded at an early age probably led to an overestimate of deflection. He concluded that, in this case, early loading does not significantly change the total final deflection and the critical condition is collapse.

In the second case, the design limit state was that of deflection. At early age, the moment applied was equal to two-thirds of the resistance moment at that age up to a maximum moment which gave a deflection of 1/250th of the span. This was normally reached after 7 days. At early age, the applied moment was a higher percentage of the limiting moment than in the first pattern of loading, and this resulted in increased differences between the calculated and measured deflections. Allowing for the conservative nature of the calculated creep deflection, Sadgrove estimated that loading the beam, when it had achieved 13, 27, 40 and 67% of its specified characteristic strength, increased the total deflection by 25, 25, 9 and 3% respectively.

The following factors should be considered:

1. The self-weight of a slab is unlikely to fall below 40% of the total design load and, on the basis of Sadgrove's collapse criterion, this requires the concrete to have achieved at least 40% of its characteristic strength before striking. The increase in deflection is therefore unlikely to exceed 10%.

2. Most beams and slabs are designed as under-reinforced members, and they therefore gain stiffness more quickly than predicted by calculations based on a balanced section.

3. The concrete strength [and therefore stiffness] is usually greater than assumed, because the characteristic strength of the concrete is usually exceeded.

These considerations indicate that provided the applied load does not exceed two-thirds of the ultimate load at that age, deflection is not significantly increased by early loading. Sadgrove's collapse criterion of matching the proportion of the load applied to the proportion of the characteristic strength achieved, therefore also satisfies the deflection criterion.

Samuelsson[6] showed that a strength of 10 N/mm^2 from cubes of equal maturity to in-situ concrete keeps deflections within acceptable limits and prevents marking when forms are stripped.

3.3 FREEZE/THAW DAMAGE

Within a sealed container, the hydration of concrete is a process of self-desiccation and the volume occupied by the hydration product is less than the volume of the original cement grains and water. During hydration, voids are therefore created within the cement paste. As hydration proceeds, less free water remains to be frozen, and a point is reached where freezing causes little damage to the concrete.

In practice, concrete members are not cast in sealed containers, and it is seldom possible to measure capillary space. The difference between concrete enclosed in formwork and the experimental simulation with sealed containers is often small, but it is necessary to define the pre-hardening period in which concrete should not be frozen, in easily measurable terms. Sadgrove examined this in a series of experiments[7], and he demonstrated that when the concrete attains a compressive strength of 2 N/mm^2 before freezing, subsequent freezing does not cause serious damage to the concrete. This conclusion is independent of the concrete mix and the freezing régime. Guidance in this report is based on a 2 N/mm^2 criterion, but it should be noted that BS8110[14] suggests a more conservative value of 5 N/mm^2. This recommendation is not applicable to the situation where water in addition to the initial mix water (e.g. rain) has entered the concrete prior to freezing. Saturated concretes require a considerably higher strength to resist the effects of freezing.

3.4 MECHANICAL DAMAGE TO THE CONCRETE BY THE REMOVAL OF FORMWORK

The assumptions are made that the formwork has been well designed and constructed, and that the striking is carried out with care. If adhesion between the form face and the concrete is greater than the cohesion in the concrete, damage occurs on striking. This damage takes the form of scaling of the concrete surfaces and spalled arrises. The damage can vary from the structurally significant (in that the cover to reinforcement is seriously reduced) to slight scaling over large aggregate which is only visible on very close inspection.

A study of this subject[8] showed that the concrete strength at striking and the type of form face had a significant influence, as did the presence of a release agent. Neither the concrete mix proportions nor the type of release agent were significant. Figure 3.1 enables the mechanical damage striking criterion to be selected to suit the particular requirement. The real time to formwork striking can be calculated from the equivalent age at 20°C (see Section 4.2). For the high class F3 and F4 finishes[27], the appropriate equivalent age for striking is 12 hours for oiled, unsealed plywood and 10 hours for oiled, impermeable formwork. With the basic F1 and F2 finishes, the times may be reduced, but they should not be less than 8 and 6 hours, respectively, because the damage might then be structurally significant.

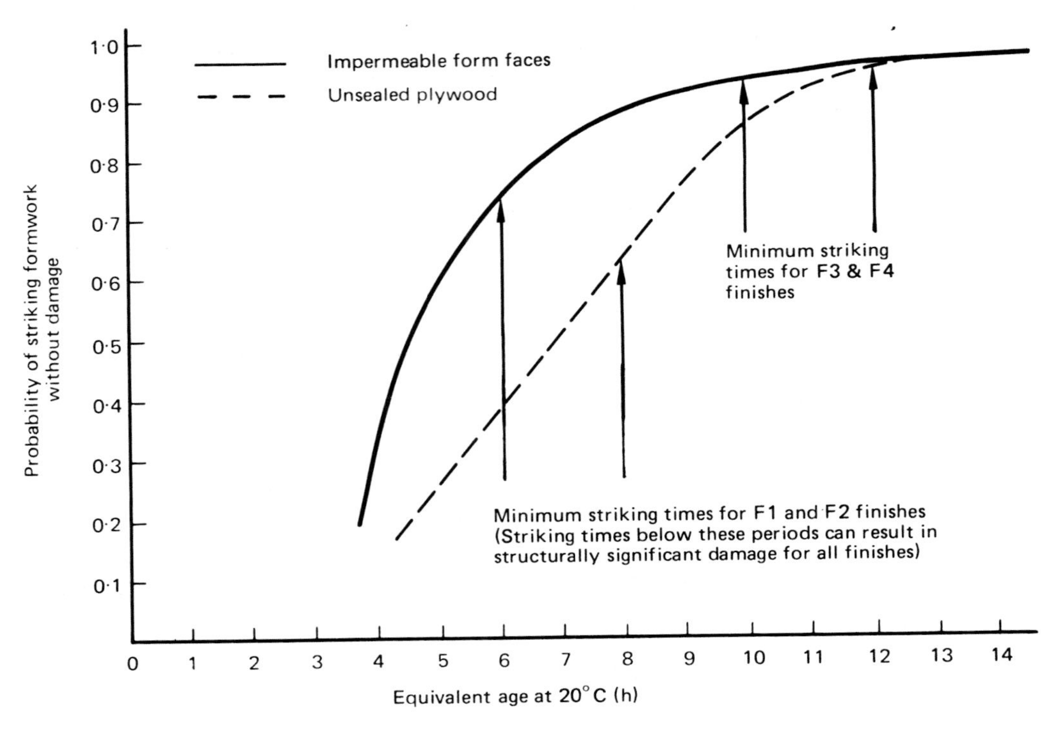

Figure 3.1 *Probability of striking formwork without mechanical damage to the concrete surface*

To cater for low strength concrete, and for its coincidence with the freeze/thaw damage criterion, the striking criterion for vertical F3 and F4 finishes is more easily defined as a minimum in-situ cube strength of 2 N/mm^2.

Provided that there is no risk of freeze/thaw damage, it is inappropriate to restrict the striking times for F1 and F2 finishes by imposing a 2 N/mm^2 strength requirement.

There can be considerable difficulty in striking formwork for some types of special finish. In particular, deep, closely-spaced ribs are almost impossible to strike without some damage. The dilemma is that the stronger the concrete is at striking, the less is the chance of damage to the concrete, but the greater the likelihood of damaging the form. Also, visually satisfactory repairs become more difficult as the concrete matures.

Constructing a trial panel[12] to see if the finish is obtainable might be necessary. Striking when the concrete is expected to have an in-situ cube strength of 2 N/mm^2 is a good starting point with many types of finish.

3.5 FURTHER MECHANICAL DAMAGE

Economics dictate that formwork cannot be left in place to protect the concrete from further mechanical damage. If necessary, alternative protection can be given with arris strips, or by barriers. These techniques are no substitutes for care by all operatives working near the exposed concrete.

3.6 MOISTURE LOSS

The gain of strength of concrete is subject to there being sufficient available water in the concrete for the continued hydration of the cement paste. If insufficient water is present, the rate of hydration slows down, and if the relative humidity inside the cement paste falls to below 85%, the gain of strength of the concrete virtually ceases[28]. When the dry concrete is re-wetted, hydration continues, but the coarsening of the porosity caused by severe early drying is not, in general, recoverable.

Formwork tends to retain moisture within the concrete, and with its early removal a subsequent method of retaining the moisture might be required. See BS 8110[14] for minimum periods of curing and protection.

In the prediction of striking times for slabs, it is assumed that the upper surface is covered, so that any loss of water from the surface is not sufficient to affect the rate of hydration of the cement.

3.7 COLOUR VARIATION

Consistency in striking times helps to minimise colour variation.

3.8 DURABILITY

There is a relationship between lack of surface durability and inadequate curing. However, provided curing is maintained, early striking of formwork has no significant effect on durability.

3.9 THERMAL CRACKING AND SHOCK

The mechanisms of early-age thermal cracking are described in CIRIA Report 91[29]. In essence cracking occurs when the restrained thermal contraction exceeds the tensile strain capacity of the concrete.

Restraint to movement can be caused either internally or externally. For example, removing the formwork while the concrete is still hot allows the surface to cool rapidly. The consequent contraction of the surface is restrained by the still hot interior and surface cracking results. The extreme case of this phenomenon is called 'thermal shock' - its occurrence is rare in the U.K.

Another example of internal restraint is in large sections when the formwork has high conductance. The concrete near the surface hardens at a lower temperature than the concrete in the centre. When all the concrete eventually cools to ambient temperature, the surface zone restrains the central zone from contracting, and internal cracking results. It may be specified that large isolated pours are insulated, and that the insulation must be left in place until the whole mass of concrete has cooled to some defined temperature. This is likely to take up to two weeks and therefore, if specified, generally controls the time at which formwork is removed.

The presence of re-entrant angles may require formwork to be removed as soon as possible after concrete has set to avoid cracking as it cools (see BS 8110, Section 6).

3.10 SITE REQUIREMENTS

Formwork is usually stripped as quickly as possible, but there are situations where it is not required for a few days. Parts of the system are then less likely to be mislaid if they are still surrounding another structure.

3.11 SUMMARY OF METHODS OF DETERMINING THE CONCRETE STRENGTH REQUIRED FOR STRIKING

3.11.1 Soffit formwork using Sadgrove's relationship

1. Calculate the load from self-weight.
2. Determine the construction load.
3. Express the sum of the self-weight and construction load as a proportion of the design working load.
4. Multiply the above proportion by the grade of concrete used for structural design to obtain the characteristic strength of cubes of equal maturity to the in-situ concrete required before the forms may be removed.
5. Obtain striking time from Tables 4.6 to 4.8 or multiply by 1.25 to obtain the mean strength required for temperature-matched cubes or other forms of in-situ testing.

3.11.2 Soffit formwork by analysis of the actual section

This method is advantageous for lightly reinforced sections where section size is not determined by concrete strength, i.e. under-reinforced sections.

1. Determine which adjoining sections are completed giving continuity of structural action.
2. Determine the design load from 1.2 times dead load plus 1.2 times the construction load.
3. Calculate the characteristic strength using the normal methods of analysis. Remember to check bond strength. Do not use the shear formulae in BS 8110 below about 10 N/mm^2.
4. Obtain striking time from Tables 4.6 to 4.8 or multiply by 1.25 to obtain the mean strength required for temperature-matched cubes or other forms of in-situ testing.

3.11.3 Vertical formwork

The striking time is the greatest value derived from consideration of the relevant items of the four given below:

1. Check wind loading, using Appendix A or by calculation to obtain the required strength.

2. If freeze/thaw damage is possible, a minimum in-situ cube strength of 2 N/mm^2 is required.

3. Mechanical damage

   (a) F3 and F4 finishes - a minimum value in-situ cube strength of 2 N/mm^2 is required

   (b) F1 and F2 finishes - a minimum period equivalent to 8 hours at 20°C for unsealed plywood formwork, or 6 hours at 20°C for impermeable formwork is required.

4. If thermal cracking is important, special techniques might be necessary which could control the striking time[(29)].

4 Predicting the strength of concrete

4.1 INTRODUCTION

The mathematical and computational techniques for predicting the maturity[30-42] and hence the strength of concrete are so good that the quality of the prediction depends almost entirely on the quality of the input data. For example 15 years of experience with the Danish system, CIMS[42], has shown that if the assumptions about input values are correct, the predicted and measured temperatures are within 2.5°C.

Predictive methods are useful for job programming purposes, but they should not provide the only input into a decision to remove formwork: some additional checking is essential. On rare occasions, the concrete may not be as intended, or the in-situ heating systems may breakdown. Therefore one of the methods described in Sections 6.2 to 6.7 should be used in conjunction with a predictive method.

In Scandinavia where the use of predictive methods is well established, the contractor and concrete producer work together to provide concrete mixes that permit the forms to be removed at pre-determined times. Basically, knowing the section dimensions, the type of formwork, applied heating (if any) and the weather forecast, the producer using a software package determines the concrete quality needed to provide the necessary strength at the pre-determined striking time.

4.2 MATURITY

Cube strength is a function of the concrete mix proportions, the time between casting and testing, and the temperature(s) at which the cube was stored. Therefore, for a particular mix, it should be possible to produce a relationship between time and temperature to predict maturity and strength. This is the purpose of maturity laws. From the measured or calculated temperature-time history at a point in a concrete section, the maturity law is used to calculate the maturity at that point and hence the strength of test cubes of equal maturity to that point. Traditionally, maturities were expressed in units of °C h, but recently the trend has been to express the maturity as being equivalent to ... days at the standard curing temperature of control cubes (20°C in the U.K.).

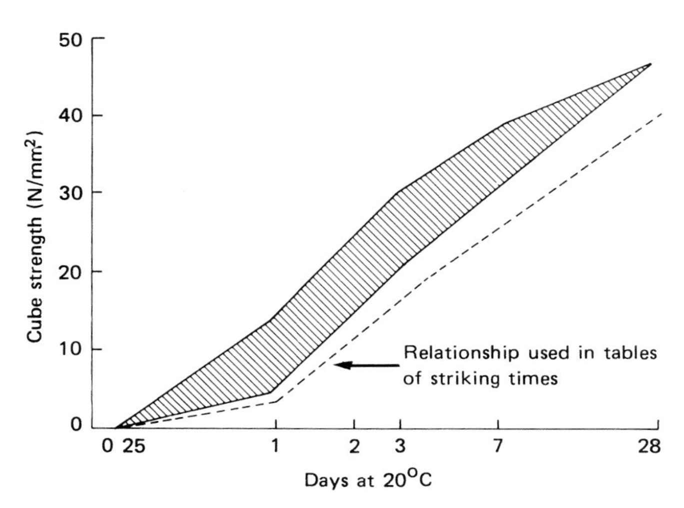

Figure 4.1 *Typical envelope of strength for PC-42.5 concretes*

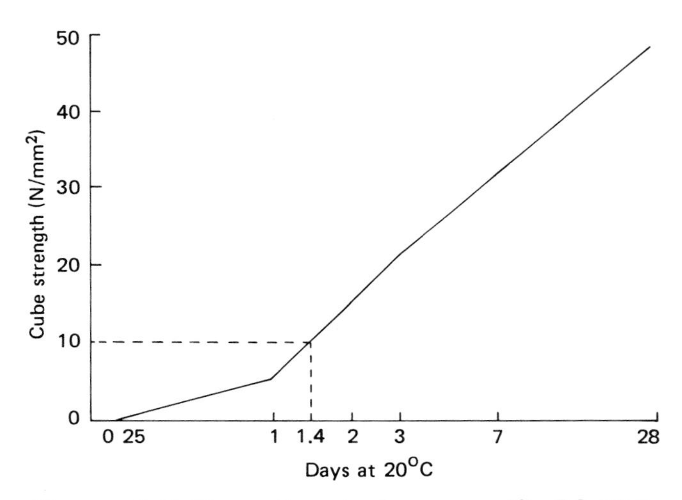

Figure 4.2 *Strength gain for a specific PC-42.5 concrete*

The relationship between strength and maturity is not unique for all concretes of a constant 28-day strength, see Figure 4.1, and therefore it has to be determined experimentally for the particular concrete being used. This is most easily achieved by crushing cubes which have been stored in water at 20°C at 1, 2, 3, 7 and 28 days to obtain the strength development curve for the specific concrete mix, Figure 4.2. Then, if the formwork striking times criteria requires, say, 10 N/mm^2 from cubes of equal maturity to the structure, this equates to a maturity of at least 1.4 days at 20°C, Figure 4.2.

The maturity laws follow the same basic equation of

$$\text{Equivalent age at } 20°C = \Sigma k \Delta t \qquad [4.1]$$

The objective of the maturity law is to produce an equation for maturity function, k, so that samples of a particular concrete with equal maturity have equal strength, regardless of the actual temperature-time history. Numerous laws have been proposed[43-50], of which the majority were derived empirically. In recent years, laws have been developed based on the concept of activation energy and the Arrhenius law on the rate of reaction. This equation takes the form

Equivalent age at 20°C

$$= \sum\left[\exp\left[\frac{E}{R}\left(\frac{1}{293} - \frac{1}{\theta + 273}\right)\right]\right]\Delta t \qquad [4.2]$$

where E = Activation energy obtained experimentally, kJ/mol
R = Molar gas constant = 0.008314 kJ/°C mol
q = mean concrete temperature, °C, in time increment Δt

Different types of cement have different activation energies. Hansen and Pedersen[47] suggest that for concretes containing cements now classified as PC-42.5 or 52.5, equation [4.2] becomes

Equivalent age at 20°C for values of θ of 20°C or greater

$$= \sum\left[\exp\left[\frac{33.5}{0.008314}\left(\frac{1}{293} - \frac{1}{\theta + 273}\right)\right]\right]\Delta t$$

or

Equivalent age at 20°C for values of θ below 20°C

$$= \sum\left[\exp\left[\frac{33.5 + 1.47(20 - \theta)}{0.008314}\right]\left[\frac{1}{293} - \frac{1}{\theta + 273}\right]\right]\Delta t$$

Tables of maturity function have been published[48,49] to help simplify the calculation.

For a given type of cement, empirical equations are available such as the Sadgrove equation:

$$\textit{Equivalent age at 20°C} = \sum\left(\frac{\theta + 16}{36}\right)^2 \Delta t \qquad [4.3]$$

which is valid for PC-42.5 or 52.5 concretes in the temperature range 1 to 45°C for equivalent ages at 20°C from 5h to 28d[50]. Table 4.1 shows that this gives results very similar to those produced from the activation energy equations up to 40°C.

Table 4.1 *Comparison of "k" values for Portland cement-42.5 and 52.5 concretes, obtained from equations [4.2] and [4.3]*

Temperature, °C	Equation [4.2]	Equation [4.3]
0	0.15	0.20
10	0.50	0.52
20	1.00	1.00
30	1.57	1.63
40	2.41	2.42
50	3.59	3.36
60	5.22	4.46
70	7.42	5.71

The Sadgrove equation may be applied to other cement types in a more restrictive range of temperatures. Nicklinson[51] has used the Sadgrove equation with cements containing ggbs down to 10°C. Analysis of published data[52], Appendix B, shows that at 40% ggbs, the Sadgrove equation can be applied to some combinations up to about an equivalent age of 7 days. At 70% ggbs, the Sadgrove equation may not give a safe relationship below 20°C e.g. in thin sections and therefore it is recommended that in these circumstances the linear maturity law described below is applied.

There is little guidance on the use of the Sadgrove equation with cements containing a proportion of pfa. Dhir[53] concluded that maturity laws cannot be applied to concretes containing pfa, but a re-analysis of the data published in his report, see Appendix C, indicates that the Sadgrove equation may be used in the temperature range 5 to 30°C.

Equation 4.2 can be applied to concretes containing cements with up to 10% silica fume in the temperature range 5 to 35°C[54] and as the "k" values for the Sadgrove equation and activation energy equation are similar in the range 5 to 40°C, it can be concluded that the Sadgrove equation can also be applied to concretes containing these cements.

An example of a hand calculation of maturity is given in Appendix D. If maturity is to be calculated frequently, the use of a spreadsheet is recommended.

Given the very wide range of types and classes of cements, combinations, additions and admixtures, it is important that an appropriate or safe maturity law is selected. A maturity function where $k = \theta/20$ is considered to be a safe relationship in the strength range for formwork striking with any normal cement (including those with ggbs) and therefore in the absence of data, this function could be used. This or some other selected maturity law can be checked experimentally by curing cubes at, say, 5°C, 20°C and 40°C, crushing them at intervals of time and plotting the results as a graph of cube strength against equivalent age at 20°C, see Appendix B. The selected curing temperatures should span the likely range of in-situ temperatures as it is inadvisable to extrapolate. If all the results fall on the same line, the selected maturity law is appropriate for that concrete mix. When this ideal is not achieved, but the selected maturity law underestimates the strength development, it will provide a safe solution.

4.3 PREDICTIVE METHODS

Some predictive methods[30-42] use the relationship:

Temperature rise, Δq, at an element within a section in a time Δt

= (Heat generated in element in Δt + Heat gained by element in Δt - Heat lost from element in Δt)/(Thermal capacity of the element) [4.4]

The simplicity of this equation does not reveal the complexity of its solution. The easier part is the determination of the thermal capacity. This is the product of:

the volume of the element, m^3;
the density of the element, kg/m^3;
the specific heat of the element, kJ/kg°C.

The specific heat of concrete comprises the weighted specific heats of the components of the mix, Table 4.2. All the components of normal weight concrete have similar specific heats except for the mix water which is greater by a factor of 5.

Table 4.2 *Specific heats of concrete and its components*

Component	Specific heat, kJ/kg°C
Cement	0.800
Quartz	0.750
Limestone	0.790
Basalt	0.850
Water	4.184
Concrete	0.800-1.200

The term "heat generated" relates to the heat of hydration produced by the reactions between cement, some additions and water. Two different approaches can be used to determine the heat generated and they both require experimental data. The first approach makes use of the measured adiabatic temperature rise for the proposed concrete mix and the second approach uses the activation energy calculated from measured isothermal conduction calorimetry data for the cement. The details of both of these approaches are given in Section 4.4.

Heat gain/loss relates to the gain/loss of heat at the boundaries of the element. In a typical element in a one-dimensional model, heat would be gained via the boundary nearest the centre of the section and lost from the boundary nearest the surface. Where additional heat is being generated from, say, heated formwork or reinforcement, or heat is being lost via cooling pipes, these conditions can be incorporated by making appropriate adjustments to the boundary conditions.

The rate at which heat flows across an element is controlled by its thermal conductivity, kJ/m°Ch. The complications of heat losses through formwork are often simplified. Each external boundary of the concrete element is allocated a coefficient of thermal transmittance. This is the reciprocal of the sum of the coefficients of thermal resistances of the surface, the insulation and the formwork. The overall coefficients of thermal transmittance for a number of typical formwork and insulating materials have been calculated and are given in Table 4.3.

Using the above principles, a computer program can calculate the time-temperature for any selected point in the structure and additionally, the maturity of the point. If the strength/maturity relatonship is known for the mix, the formwork striking criterion can be expressed in maturity terms and the program can be used to predict the time of formwork striking. As a planning tool, a program can be used to study options such as:

- different formwork materials
- different concrete mixes
- heating the concrete.

Table 4.3 *Coefficient of thermal transmittance of form face and insulating materials, kJ/m2 °Ch*

Materials	Normal exposure[1]	Severe exposure[1]
Nil	80	180
Up to 25mm steel	68	120
3mm glass reinforced plastic	57	95
50mm concrete	47	69
150mm concrete	30	37
18mm plywood	18.7	21.6
Air space[2]	16.2	18.0
37mm plywood	11.2	11.9
18mm plywood plus air space[2]	9.7	10.4
25mm glass wool	5.4	5.4
25mm expanded polystyrene	4.7	4.7
18mm plywood plus 25mm mineral wool	4.0	4.3
50mm glass wool	2.9	2.9
50mm expanded polystyrene	2.5	2.5

Notes

1. Normal and severe exposure are equivalent to wind speeds of 3 and 9 m/s.
2. 20 mm minimum enclosed by polythene sheet or similar.
   (Data based on the Chartered Institute of Building Services Engineers Guide, Part A 3, Thermal properties of building structures, 1980)
3. 3.6 kJ/m^2 °Ch = 1.0 W/m^2K

4.4 CALCULATION OF THE HEAT GENERATED

There are a number of systems where the starting point is an adiabatic temperature-time curve for the selected mix. Adiabatic conditions are created when there is no external heat gain or loss from the concrete. In these conditions all the heat of hydration is retained and the temperature continues to increase, albeit very slowly after a few days, until hydration ceases. These data are obtained using an adiabatic calorimeter, the principles of which are illustrated in Figure 4.3. A typical adiabatic curve is shown in Figure 4.4.

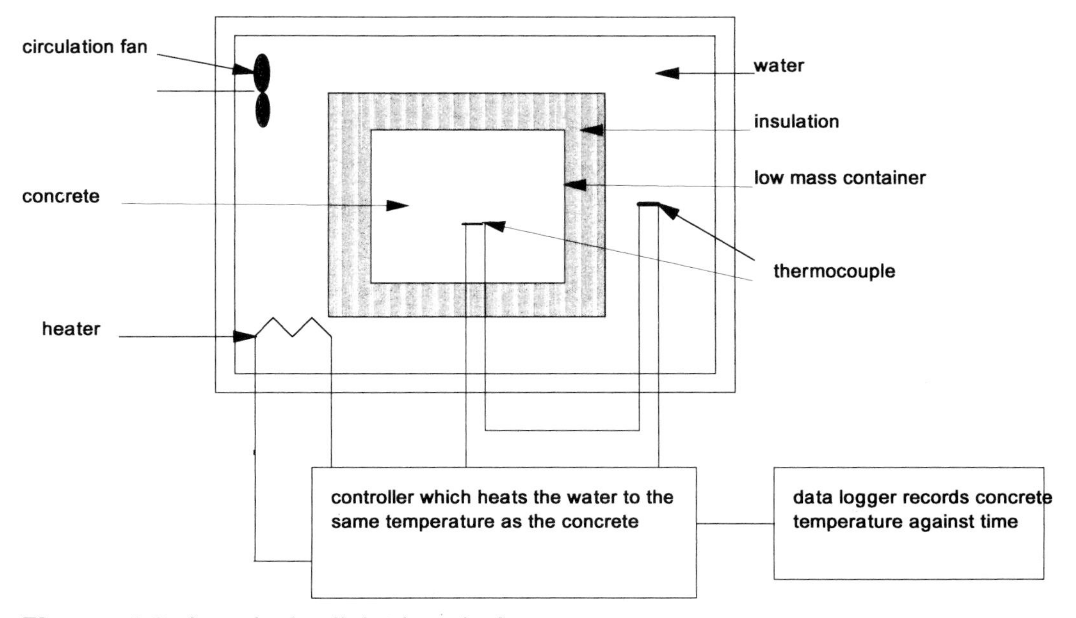

Figure 4.3 *A typical adiabatic calorimeter*

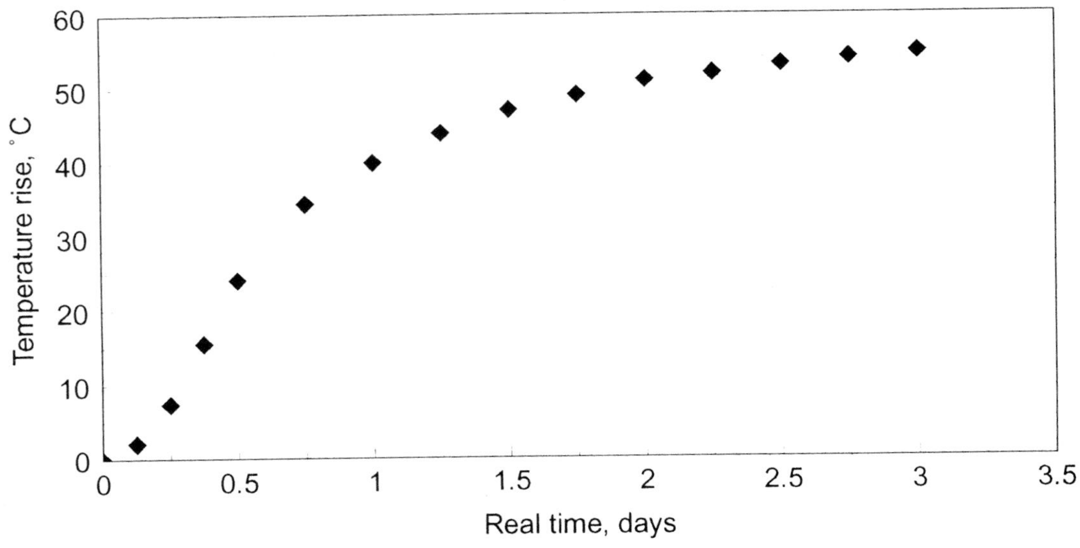

Concrete placing temperature was 18.7°C

Figure 4.4 *Adiabatic temperature rise*

How these data are utilised varies between the systems. In one system[33], the best fit exponential or S-curve is fitted directly to the data and the adiabatic temperature rise, $\Delta\theta$, after time t is given by:

$$\Delta\theta = \Delta\theta_{max}\left(1 - \exp - \left[\frac{t - t_d}{t_c}\right]\right) \quad [4.5]$$

where t = Selected time
t_d = Dormant period
t_c = Time constant

To avoid excessive testing, $\Delta\theta_{max}$ can be estimated for different mix proportions using:

$$\Delta\theta_{max} = \frac{W \times C \times H_{g\,max}}{c \times D_c} \quad [4.6]$$

In another system[34,41], the adiabatic temperature-time curve is replotted after converting the temperature to heat and the real time to equivalent age at 20°C, Figure 4.5.

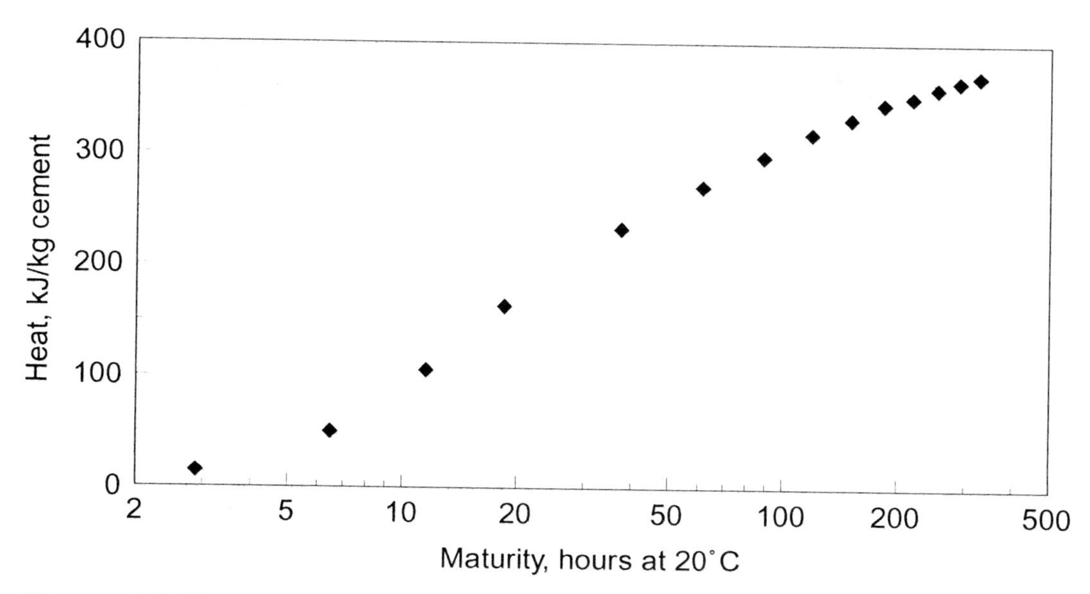

Figure 4.5 *Heat per kg cement against maturity*

An exponential curve is then fitted to the data and this relates heat to maturity by:

$$Q = Q_c \times \exp\left[-\left(\frac{\tau_e}{M}\right)^a\right] \quad [4.7]$$

This well-established method uses both strength/maturity and heat/maturity relationships, but it is important to note that the constants are not the same and the program calculates and stores both maturities.

An alternative approach to estimating the heat generated in the concrete is to use isothermal conduction calorimetry data on the cement(32,39), Figure 4.6. The outputs from this calorimeter are the rates of heat evolution, Figure 4.7, which are integrated to give total heat curves. The cement should be tested at, at least, two temperatures which ideally embrace the range of temperatures in the hydrating concrete section.

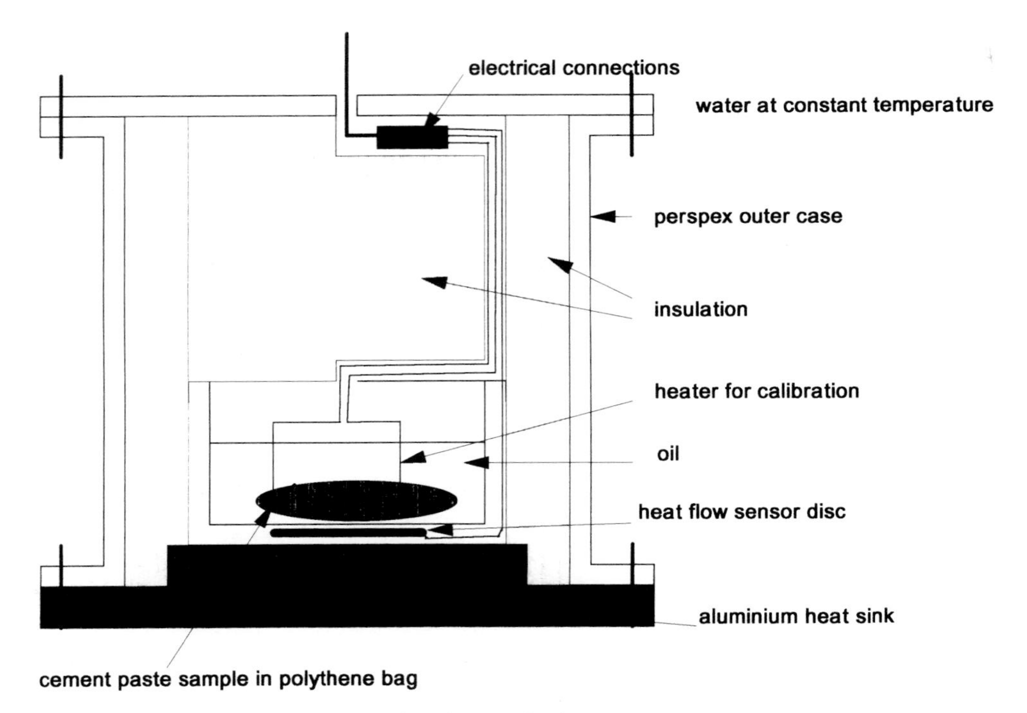

Figure 4.6 *Isothermal conduction calorimeter*

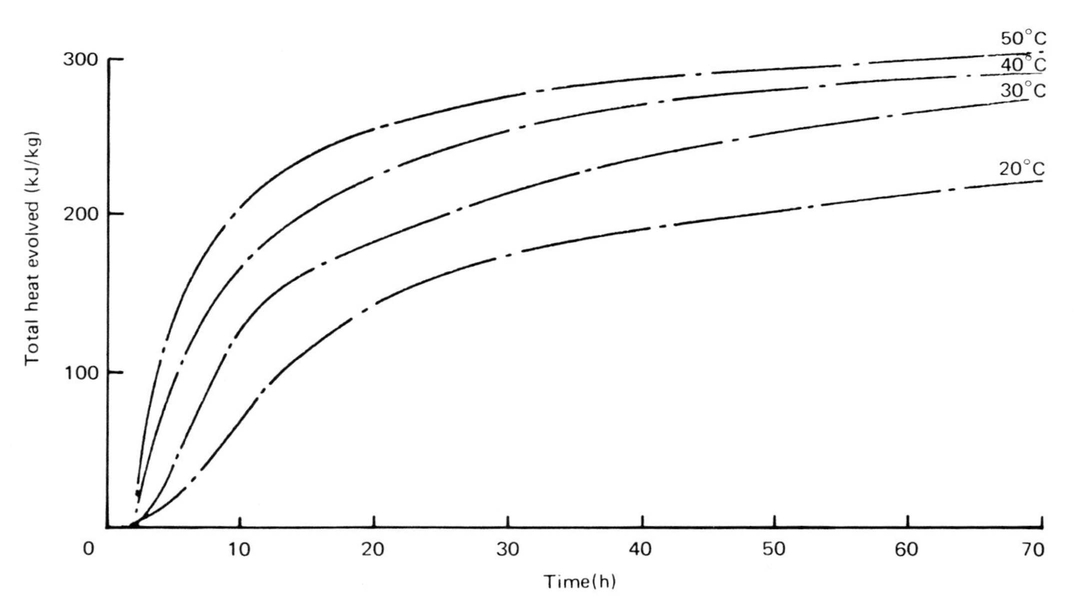

Figure 4.7 *Rates of heat evolution from cement under isothermal conditions*

An example of how these data are used is at fixed 10 kJ/kg steps of Q, the equation:

$$\log_e \frac{dQ}{dt} = -\frac{E}{R} \times \frac{1}{\theta} + a \qquad [4.8]$$

is solved for E and a. The constant "a" varies with the extent of hydration. The variations in E and a with the heat evolved are stored in memory and used to calculate the heat evolved at each point of the concrete section.

Tables 4.6, 4.7 and 4.8 are extracted from CIRIA Report 67[11]. The variations in heat generated with temperature were based on a modified Rastrup function[55]. Any errors introduced by this simplified approach are relatively small and did not warrant the development of new tables.

4.5 PREDICTION OF FORMWORK STRIKING TIMES USING JOB-SPECIFIC DATA

Any of the modern systems are capable of giving good predictions of formwork striking times if the input data are available for the specific job. This is best illustrated with some examples of the predicted and measured temperature- time curves, Figures 4.8 and 4.9.

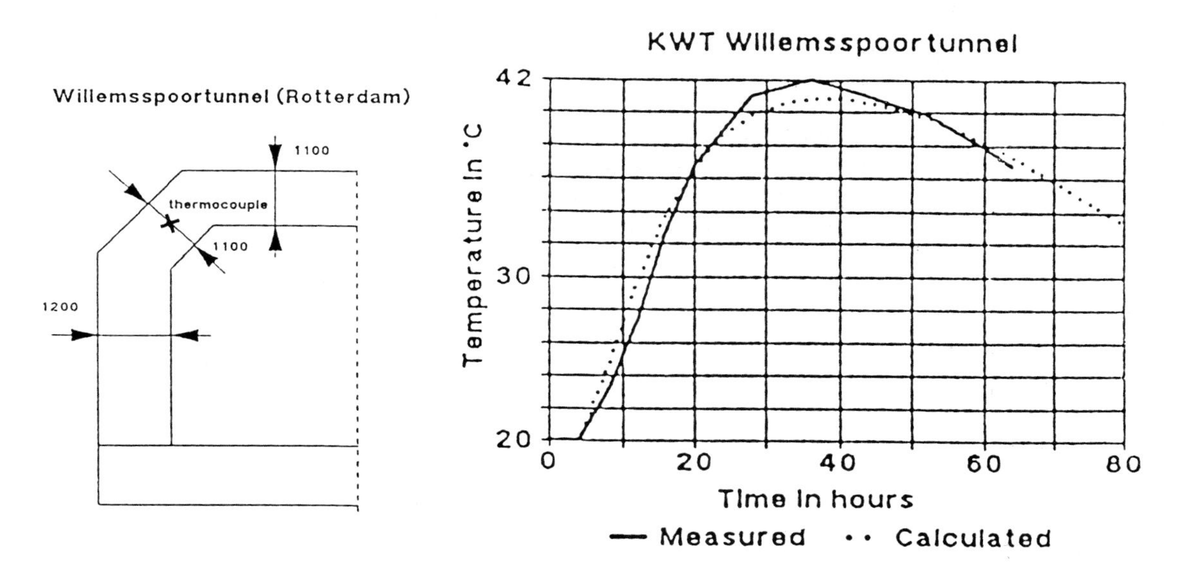

Figure 4.8 *An example of measured and predicted temperatures using Concrete Hardening Control System taken from reference 33*

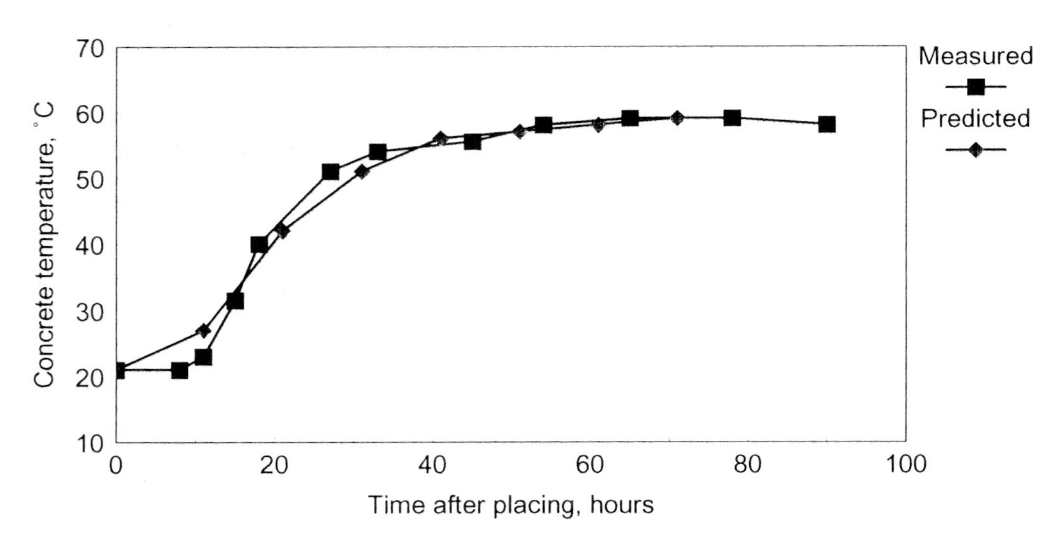

Figure 4.9 *Measured and predicted temperatures using the BCA system for a UK construction*

4.6 PREDICTION OF FORMWORK STRIKING TIMES USING NON JOB-SPECIFIC DATA

In many practical situations, for example, at tender, job-specific data are not available. However local concrete producers may be able to supply typical data for the area.

Figure 4.1 illustrates the problems created by not having job-specific data. The envelope of strength gain for one type and class of cement is wide. For example the maturity needed to achieve $10N/mm^2$ varies from 0.5 to 1.4 days at 20°C. When other cement types and classes are added, the area within the envelope increases. There are no published national data to define all these strength development envelopes. Even if these were available, their use would be limited, as at a specific site the concrete mix may be near the top or the bottom of the range.

A solution is to recognise that concrete can be specified to include construction requirements as well as the long term requirements for strength and durability. The required concrete strength(s) for striking formwork will be known at the planning stage as will the section sizes and the basic concrete specification. The typical ambient conditions will also have been obtained. Formwork materials, insulation and applied heating can be treated as variables, but in practice the real choices are likely to be very restricted.

An estimate is made of the maturity in the surface zone at selected formwork striking times such as 1, 2, 3 and 4 days. To be able to remove the formwork, the calculated or specified concrete strengths have to be achieved at these maturities. The concrete producer can give quotations for a range of mixes that give the required strength at these different maturities. In general, for given conditions the concrete will increase in cost as the maturity for a given strength reduces. However, as there are other aspects of a concrete specification that have to be satisfied, the price structure is unlikely to be so simple. The contractor can balance these different concrete costs against other options such as using formwork that insulates the concrete more effectively or the use of applied heating. The advantage of using computer programs even when job-specific data are not available is the ability to be able to review options quickly and cheaply. Effective formwork utilisation is likely to have a significant impact on project construction times and costs.

4.7 TABLES OF FORMWORK STRIKING TIMES

Tables of formwork striking times should be based on safe relationships between concrete strength and maturity and an appropriate maturity law. This is best illustrated with the example of CIRIA Report 67[11]. The philosophy behind these tables was that they should be based on the lower bound strength development of materials available in the UK at that time. As a consequence no note was taken of the lowest permitted early strengths in BS12 and the lower bound strength developments were obtained from a concrete mix design exercise. It was also assumed that the concrete would just achieve its characteristic strength at 28 days. The dashed line on Figure 4.1 gives the type of strength/maturity relationship used for the CIRIA tables.

Tables must always provide a safe and consequently conservative estimate of the formwork striking time and therefore methods that directly test the concrete should indicate a shorter, but still safe, time. Where short formwork striking times are needed, tables are not an appropriate method. The simplicity of tables makes them a suitable method of assessing striking times on small sites where stripping times are not unduly critical.

Tables 4.6 to 4.8 are based on the assumption that the specified concrete just achieves its characteristic strength e.g. a C30 concrete gives a 28d strength of 30 N/mm^2. *If you can be sure* that some higher strength will be achieved, it is possible to take this into account. For example, if 2d cubes made from batches of the concrete placed in the structure, then cured and tested under standard conditions indicate that the specified C30 concrete will give a 28d strength exceeding 40 N/mm^2, the striking times for the C40 concrete could be used. This is a less conservative way of using the tables and therefore it has to be used with care and understanding. For example, it would not be reasonable to assume that the strength of a particular mix will not change without warning.

Tables of formwork striking times for slab and beam soffits are given in Tables 4.6 to 4.8. These have been extracted from CIRIA Report 67[11]. They are applicable to PC-42.5, PC-52.5 concretes and to any other concrete that satisfies the following criteria:

1. The Sadgrove equation for maturity is applicable or safe (see 4.2).
2. The ratios of strength development are equal to or greater than the values given in Tables 4.4 or 4.5.

Table 4.4 *Minimum rates of strength development for the application of the PC-42.5 striking times*

Grade of concrete	20	25	30	40	50
Ratio of 1:28 day strength	0.08	0.09	0.10	0.11	0.11
Ratio of 3:28 day strength	0.37	0.40	0.42	0.44	0.46
Ratio of 7:28 day strength	0.62	0.65	0.66	0.68	0.70

Table 4.5 *Minimum rates of strength development for the application of the PC-52.5 striking times*

Grade of concrete	20	25	30	40	50
Ratio of 1:28 day strength	0.14	0.15	0.16	0.17	0.20
Ratio of 3:28 day strength	0.31	0.36	0.39	0.43	0.49
Ratio of 7:28 day strength	0.60	0.63	0.66	0.70	0.75

If the strength ratios equal or exceed the values in Table 4.4, the striking times for the PC-42.5 should be used and if they equal or exceed the values in Table 4.5, the striking times for the PC-52.5 may be used.

A substantial quantity of concrete used in the UK contains either pfa or ggbs as part of the binder. References 56 and 57 give general information on the influence of these materials on the strength gain of concrete. Whilst concretes containing these types of cement will often satisfy the Sadgrove equation (see 4.2) they will not always comply with the minimum rates of strength development given in Table 4.4. However in practice, the majority of concretes containing moderate amounts of these materials may satisfy the criteria, but it is essential to check.

Table 4.6 *Minimum striking times (days) for slab and beam soffits with an uninsulated top surface*

Conditions of use

1. The non-formed surfaces are cured.
2. The concrete placing temperature is at least the mean air temperature. Higher placing temperatures are not significant.
3. The table applies to any concrete that satisfies the criteria given in section 4.7.

Specified concrete	Required cube strength [N/mm^2]	Type of cement	Mean air temperature [°C] 5	10	15
Grade 20	-5	PC-52.5	5	3½	2½
	5	PC-42.5	6	4	2½
	10		9	6½	5
	15		17	13	10
Grade 25	-5	PC-52.5	4	2½	2
	5	PC-42.5	4½	3	2
	10		6½	5	4
	15		12	9	7
	20		26	19	15
Grade 30	-5	PC-52.5	3½	2	1½
	5	PC-42.5	4	2½	2
	10		5	4	3
	15		9	7	5½
	20		17	13	10
Grade 40	-5	PC-52.5	2	1½	1
	5	PC-42.5	3	2	1½
	10		3½	2½	2
	15		5	4	3
	20		8	5½	4½
	30		20	15	12
Grade 50	-5	PC-52.5	1½	1	1
	5	PC-42.5	2½	1½	1
	10		3	2	1½
	15		4	3	2½
	20		5	4	3
	30		10	8	6

Notes:

1. The minimum section dimension is not significant.
2. The assumption is made that the side forms to beams were removed when the concrete had a strength of 2 N/mm^2.
3. The table gives separate times to 5 N/mm^2 for PC-42.5 and PC-52.5. At greater strengths, the times apply to both types of cement.

Table 4.7 *Minimum striking times (days) for slab and beam soffits with 18mm plywood formwork and a 20mm enclosed air gap on the top surface*

Conditions of use

1. The concrete placing temperature is at least the mean air temperature or 5°C, whichever is the greater.
2. The side forms remain in place until the soffit is struck. If they are removed, use Table 4.6.
3. The minimum dimension is the slab depth for in-situ concrete or the slab depth less the depth of precast units for composite construction.

Specified concrete	Required cube strength [N/mm²]	Type of cement	Minimum section dimension [mm]											
			300 or under				500				1000			
			Mean air temperature [°C]											
			0	5	10	15	0	5	10	15	0	5	10	15
Grade 20	-5	PC-52.5	8	5	3	2	7	4	2½	2	5½	4	2½	2
	5	PC-42.5	9	5½	3½	2½	8	5	3	2	6½	5	3	2
	10		13	8	6½	5	11	8	6	4½	10	7	5½	4½
	15		25	17	13	10	23	16	12	9	22	15	11	9
Grade 25	-5	PC-52.5	6½	4	2½	1½	5	3	2	1½	4	3	2	1½
	5	PC-42.5	7	4½	3	2	6	3½	2½	3½	5	3½	2	1½
	10		10	6½	5	4	8	5½	4½	3½	7	5	4	3
	15		18	12	9	7	16	11	8	6½	14	10	8	6
	20		†	25	19	15	†	24	18	15	†	23	17	14
Grade 30	-5	PC-52.5	5	3	2	1½	4	2½	1½	1	3	2	1½	1
	5	PC-42.5	6	3½	2½	1½	4½	3	2	1½	4	2½	2	1½
	10		7	5	3½	3	6	4	3	2½	5	4	3	2½
	15		13	9	6½	5½	12	8	6	5	10	7	5½	4½
	20		26	17	13	10	24	16	12	10	22	15	11	9
Grade 40	-5	PC-52.5	3	2	1½	1	2½	1½	1	1	2	1½	1	1
	5	PC-42.5	5	3	2	1½	3½	2½	1½	1	3	2	1½	1
	10		6	3½	2½	2	4	3	2	1½	3½	2½	2	1½
	15		7	5	3½	3	5½	4	3	2½	4½	3½	3	2½
	20		11	7	5½	4½	9	6½	5	4	7	5½	4	3½
	30		†	20	15	12	27	18	14	11	25	17	13	10
Grade 50	-5	PC-52.5	2½	1½	1	½	1½	1½	1	½	1½	1½	1	½
	5	PC-42.5	3½	2	1½	1	2½	2	1	1	2	1½	1	1
	10		4	2½	2	1½	3	2½	1½	1½	2½	2	1½	1½
	15		5	3½	2½	2	4	3	2	2	3½	2½	2	2
	20		7	5	3½	3	5½	4	3	2½	4½	3½	3	2½
	30		15	10	7	6	12	8	6½	5	10	7	5½	4½

† Strength not reached within 28 days from casting

Note:
1. The table gives separate times to 5 N/mm² for PC-42.5 and PC-52.5. At greater strengths, the times apply to both types of cement.

Table 4.8 *Minimum striking times (days) for slab and beam soffits with 25mm expanded polystyrene on all surfaces*

Conditions of use

1. The concrete placing temperature is at least the mean air temperature or 5°C, whichever is the greater.
2. The insulation remains in place until the soffit is struck. If it is removed, use Table 4.6.
3. The minimum dimension is the slab depth for in-situ concrete or the slab depth less the depth of precast units for composite construction.

Specified concrete	Required cube strength [N/mm²]	Type of cement	Minimum section dimension [mm]																		
			100				300					500					1000				
			Mean air temperature [°C]																		
			0	5	10	15	-5	0	5	10	15	-5	0	5	10	15	-5	0	5	10	15
Grade 20	-5	PC-52.5	6	4	2½	1½	7	4	3	2	1½	4½	3½	3	2	1½	3½	3	3	2	1½
	5	PC-42.5	7	4½	3	2	9	5	3½	2½	2	5	4	3	2½	2	4	3½	3	2½	2
	10		11	8	6	4½	14	8	6	5	4	9	7	5½	4½	3½	6½	5½	5	4	3½
	15		24	16	12	9	†	20	14	10	8	†	16	12	9	7	15	12	10	8	7
Grade 25	-5	PC-52.5	4½	3	2	1½	4½	3	2½	1½	1½	3	2½	2½	1½	1½	2½	2½	2½	1½	1
	5	PC-42.5	5	3	2	1½	5½	3½	3	2	1½	3½	3	2½	2	1½	3	3	2½	2	1½
	10		8	5½	4½	3½	9	6	4½	3½	3	6	5	4	3½	2½	4½	4	4	3	2½
	15		16	11	8	6½	22	13	9	7	5½	15	10	8	6	5	9	8	6½	5½	4½
	20		†	24	18	15	†	†	22	16	13	†	27	19	14	12	†	19	15	12	10
Grade 30	-5	PC-52.5	3	2	1½	1	3	2½	2	1½	1	2½	2	2	1½	1	2	2	2	1½	1
	5	PC-42.5	4	2½	2	1½	4	3	2½	1½	1	3	2½	2	1½	1	2½	2½	2	1½	1
	10		6	4	3	2½	5½	4	3½	2½	2	4	3½	3	2½	2	3½	3½	3	2½	2
	15		12	8	6	5	14	8	6½	5	4	8	6½	5½	4½	3½	6	5½	5	4	3½
	20		24	16	12	10	†	19	13	10	8	26	15	11	9	7	13	10	9	7	6
Grade 40	-5	PC-52.5	2	1½	1	1	2	1½	1½	1	1	1½	1½	1½	1	1	1½	1½	1	1	1
	5	PC-42.5	3	2	1½	1	3	2	2	1½	1	2½	2	2	1½	1	2	2	2	1½	1
	10		4	3	2	2	3½	2½	2½	2	1½	3	3	2½	2	1½	2½	2½	2½	2	1½
	15		5½	4	3	2½	5	3½	3	2½	2	3½	3½	3	2½	2	3½	3	3	2½	2
	20		9	6½	5	4	9	6	4½	3½	3	5½	4½	4	3½	3	4½	4	4	3	2½
	30		27	18	14	11	†	22	15	11	9	†	17	12	9	8	13	11	9	8	6½
Grade 50	-5	PC-52.5	1½	1	1	½	1½	1½	1	1	½	1½	1½	1	1	½	1½	1	1	1	½
	5	PC-42.5	2	1½	1	1	2	1½	1½	1	1	2	1½	1½	1	1	1½	1½	1½	1	1
	10		2½	2	1½	1½	2½	2	2	1½	1	2	2	2	1½	1	2	2	2	1½	1
	15		4	3	2	2	3	2½	2½	2	1½	2½	2½	2½	2	1½	2½	2½	2	2	1½
	20		5½	4	3	2½	4½	3½	3	2½	2	3½	3	3	2½	2	3	3	2½	2	2
	30		13	9	6½	5	13	8	6	4½	3½	7	6	5	4	3½	5	5	4½	3½	3

† Strength not reached within 28 days from casting

Note:

1. The table gives separate times to 5 N/mm² for PC-42.5 and PC-52.5. At greater strengths, the times apply to both types of cement

5 Reduction of formwork striking times

Formwork striking times may be reduced by expressing the striking criterion in terms of cube strength of test specimens of equal maturity to the structure then increasing the early strength of the in-situ concrete for equal maturity and/ or increasing the maturity for equal real time. The early strength can be increased by:

1. Using cements with rapid strength development[56,57].

2. Using accelerating admixtures (non-chloride admixtures should be used if the concrete contains reinforcement or embedded metal).

3. Using concretes of higher characteristic strength, Figure 5.1. Note that changes in workability have a small effect on strength gain, Figure 5.2.

As stated in 4.6, it is better if the requirement for strength at a given maturity is added to the concrete specification. This will leave the producer free to satisfy this performance requirement in the most cost effective way using their normal materials.

The maturity can be increased for any real time by:

1. Specifying a higher placing temperature of the concrete (not many concrete production units in the UK have the facility to produce heated concrete and it is more effective if it is used in conjunction with insulated formwork).

2. Increasing the insulating effectiveness of the formwork, Figure 5.3.

3. Accelerated curing of the placed concrete.

There are many systems for accelerated curing such as space heating, heating the forms or directly heating the concrete via the reinforcement. It is very important that the concrete is not over-heated as this may lead to long term durability problems[58].

The techniques used to reduce formwork striking times are generally the opposite of those needed to reduce the risks of early-age thermal cracking[29]. This may place limitations on what may be done to reduce formwork striking times.

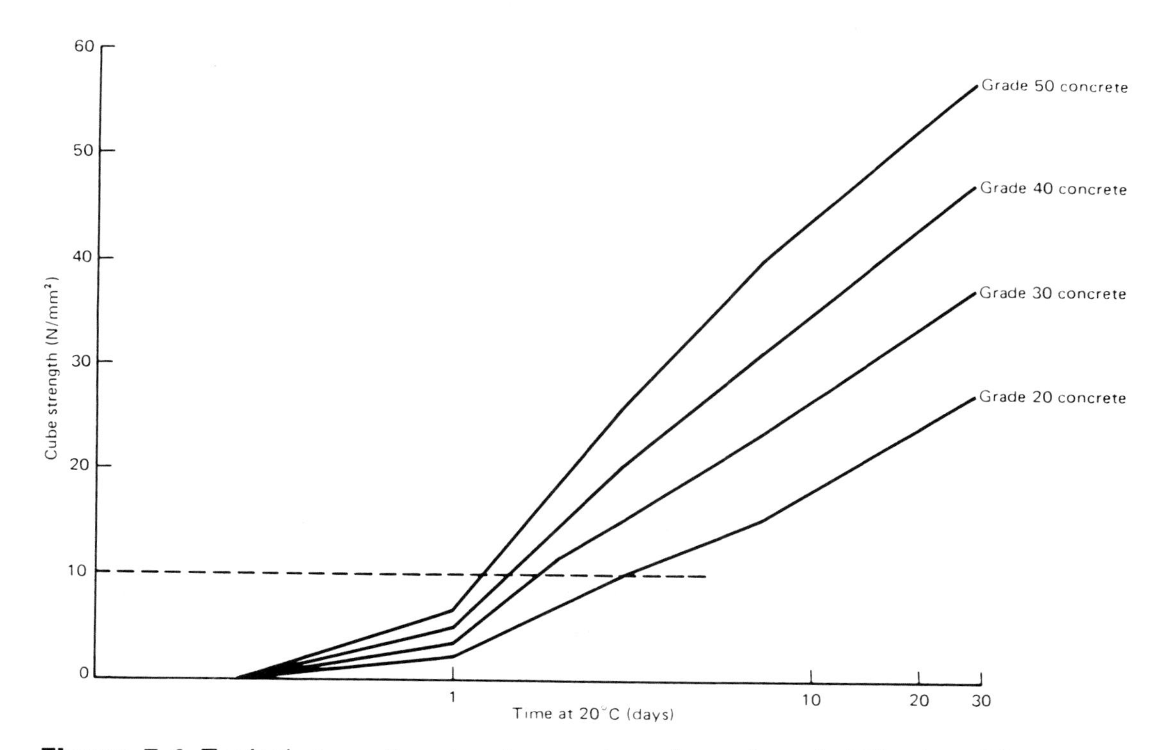

Figure 5.1 *Typical strength gain of concretes of equal workability but different grades*

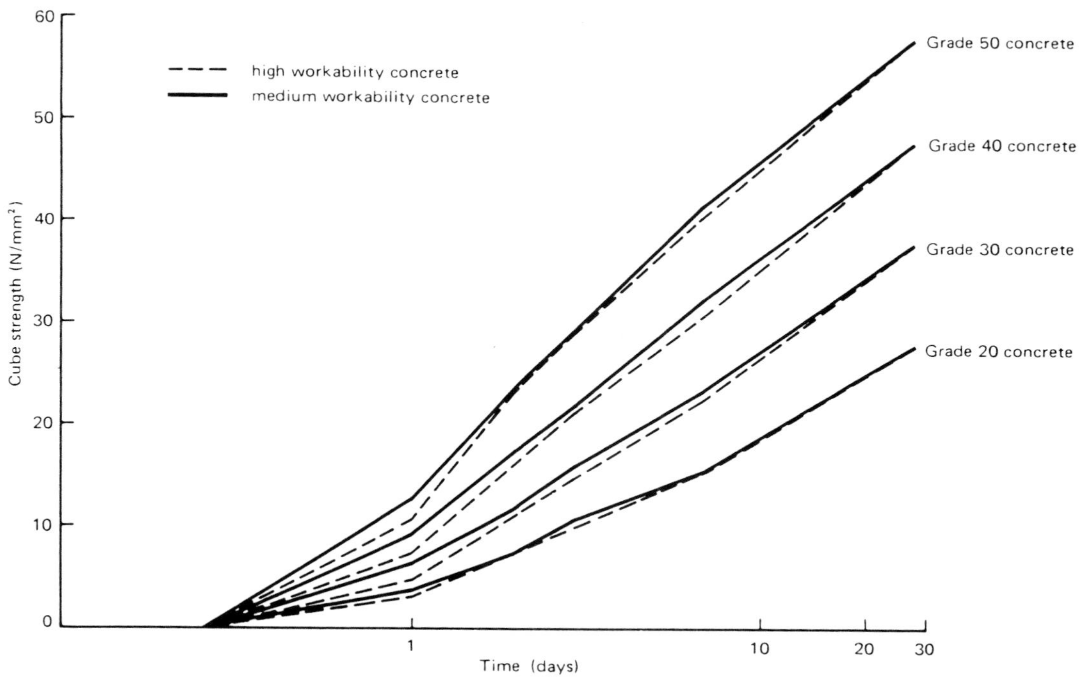

Figure 5.2 *Strength gain at 20°C of high and medium workability PC-42.5 concretes*

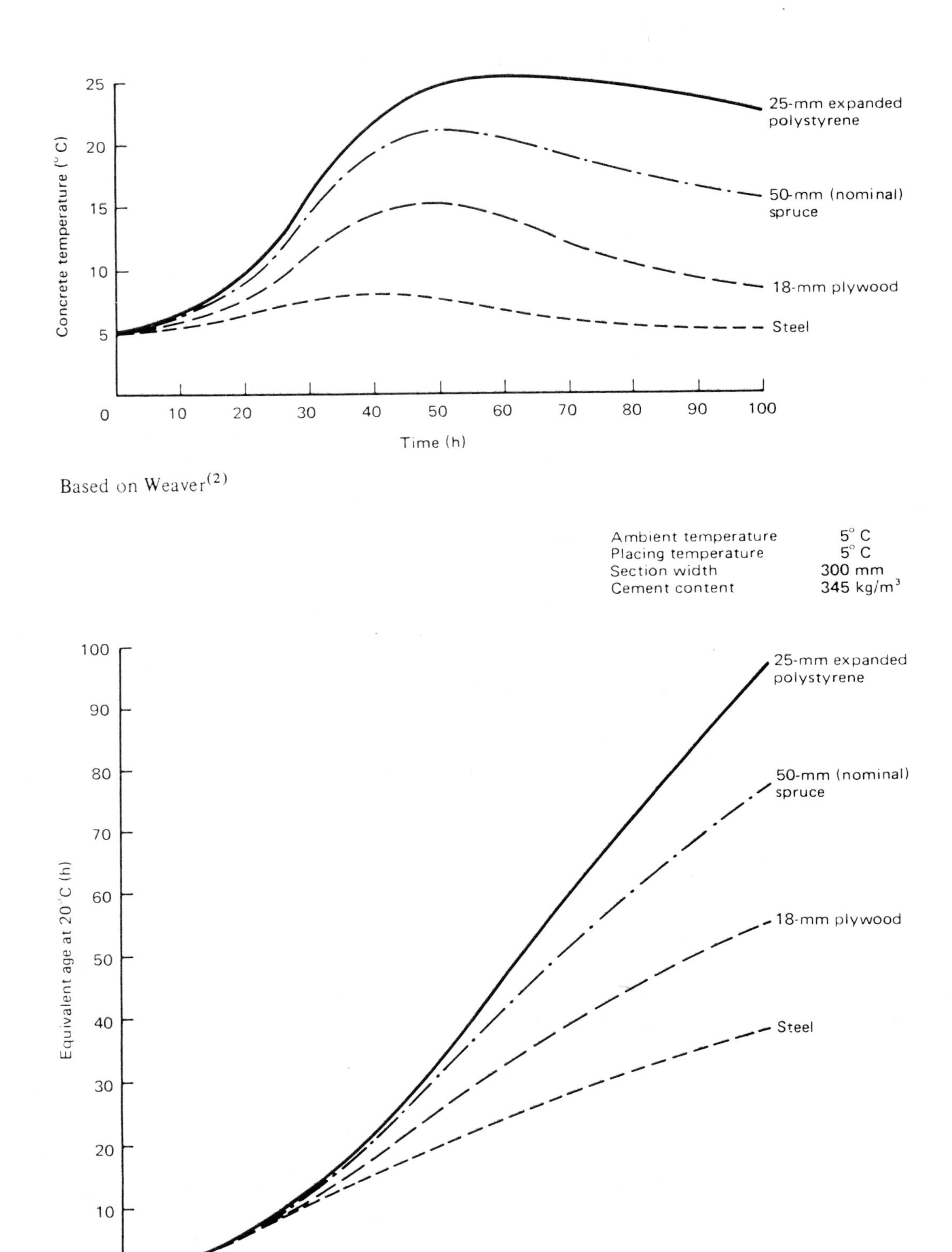

Figure 5.3 *Effect of formwork type on the temperature and equivalent age at the concrete surface*

6 Methods of determining striking times

6.1 INTRODUCTION

A number of techniques are available for determining striking times. However, they do not all indicate the same striking times, because different techniques have different degrees of conservatism built into them. In broad terms, the less sophisticated the technique, the longer is the indicated time before striking. When rapid construction is required, tables should not be used to determine the striking time. Temperature-matched cubes or one of the other in-situ test methods such as pull-out tests are appropriate. The cost benefits of saving time should significantly outweigh any modest investment in capital equipment for determining striking times. The use of tables to determine the striking times has been covered in Section 4.7.

6.2 CUBES CURED ALONGSIDE

Cubes are made from samples of the concrete used for the structure, and they are cured in conditions as near as possible to those in the structure. This is normally achieved by laying the cubes alongside or on top of the structure. If a slab is insulated, the cubes should be placed under the insulation.

The gain in strength of concrete at a given point in a structure is not only a function of the concrete and the ambient conditions, but also a function of the size and shape of a section and the insulating effectiveness of the formwork. The 'cubes cured alongside' method for determining striking times does not recognise the significance of these factors. 'Cubes cured alongside' generally have a lower maturity than the in-situ concrete.

However, with walls up to about 300 mm in thickness cast in steel- or glass-reinforced plastic formwork and most suspended slabs, the differences in maturity between cubes cured alongside and in-situ concrete are small, and therefore cubes cured alongside is an appropriate method of assessing striking times with these types of sections. This method is less appropriate with thick sections where the difference in maturity between cubes cured alongside and in-situ concrete becomes significant.

An advantage of this system is that, unlike the tabular method given in BS 8110[14], the cube strength required can be varied to suit the particular situation. The soffit striking criterion can be used to obtain the mean cube strength required. If only a few cubes have been cured alongside, a reasonable estimate of the time to test has to be made. This can be done using a predictive method or Tables 4.6 to 4.8.

The cubes cured alongside method is likely to indicate conservative striking times for large sections, thick slabs, or well-insulated vertical sections[59]. With those types of section, consideration should be given to other methods.

6.3 TEMPERATURE-MATCHED CUBES

The limitations of cubes cured alongside can be overcome with a temperature-matched curing system[59,60] (see Figure 6.1). Cubes are made from samples of the concrete placed in the element with a steel or glass plate placed on the exposed cube surface. The covered cube moulds are then submerged in the curing bath. The water in the bath (and consequently the cubes) is matched in temperature to a pre-selected location in the in-situ or precast element. The test procedure is described in DD 92[61]. A power supply is needed, also a safe place to store the controller. This system can also be used with accelerated-curing techniques and precast production, and it is likely to indicate the shortest, still safe, striking times.

6.4 PENETRATION TESTS

The best known of these tests is the Windsor Probe test[16,62,63] (see Figure 6.2). Hardened steel probes are fired into the element, and the depth of penetration is measured by measuring the length of probe protruding above the concrete surface. At least three probes should be fired into the element and the results averaged. The reliability of general calibration charts has been questioned[62], and it is recommended that the strength/exposed probe length relationship should be established for the particular concrete being tested. Problems with calibration can occur with hard aggregates in a low-strength matrix. Keiller's research[64] indicates 90% confidence limits of about ± 8 N/mm^2 for a range of mature concretes. Some data for confidence limits at in-situ cube strengths more typical of those at formwork striking (< 20 N/mm^2) are published in Reference 63, but these are based on using six probes.

The advantages of the penetration test are that it is quick, needs no prior preparation other than calibration, and the test can be repeated if necessary.

6.5 PULL-OUT TESTS

The LOK test is the best known of the pull-out tests[16,65-67]. The test consists of stressing a cast-in disc to a pre-determined value (see Figures 6.3 and 6.4). If the strength is lower than expected, the disc is pulled out of the concrete. An alternative to stressing to a pre-determined value is to test it to its pull-out value. This allows the strength over the minimum required to be calculated, and it recovers the disc for subsequent use. The testing of each insert takes about 2 min. A minimum of six inserts per structural element, or 10 inserts per 100 m^3 of slab is recommended[65]. The mean value, the standard deviations and the characteristic pull-out values are calculated. The characteristic pull-out value is then converted to mean in-situ cube strength using:

$$Cube\ strength\left[\mathrm{N}/mm^2\right]=\frac{LOK\ strength\ [k\mathrm{N}]-2.2}{0.75} \qquad [6.1]$$

This relationship only applies to normal weight concrete with a maximum aggregate size of 20 mm[65].

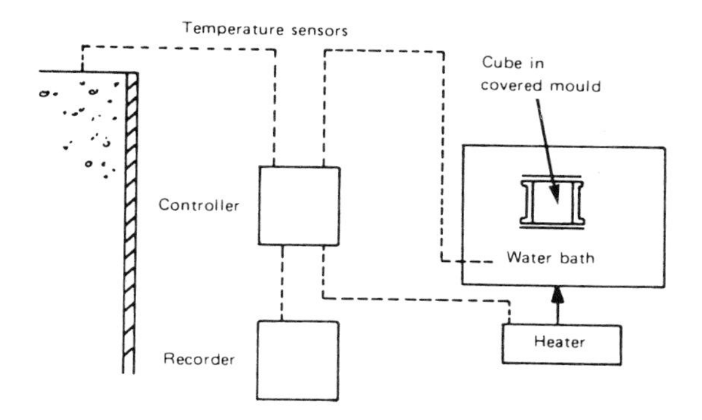

(a) Principle of the system

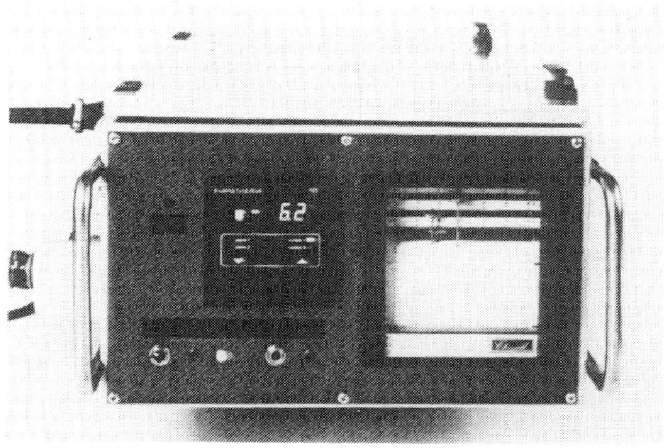

(b) Controller/Recorder

(c) Water Bath

Figure 6.1 *Temperature-matched curing*

(a) Driving the Probe into the concrete

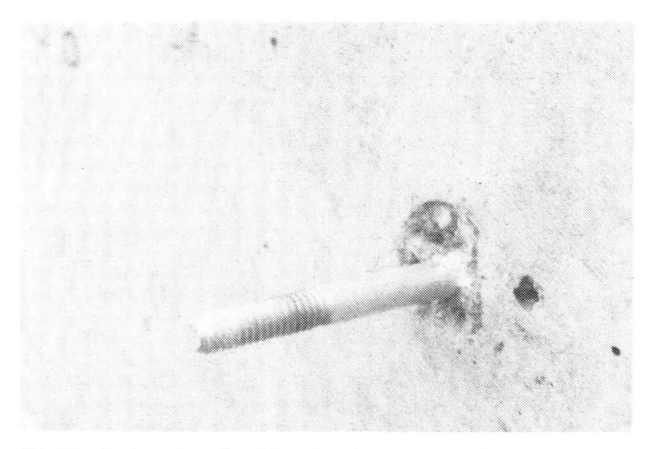

(b) The Probe after the driver has been removed

(c) Measuring the exposed length of Probe

Figure 6.2 *Windsor Probe penetration test*

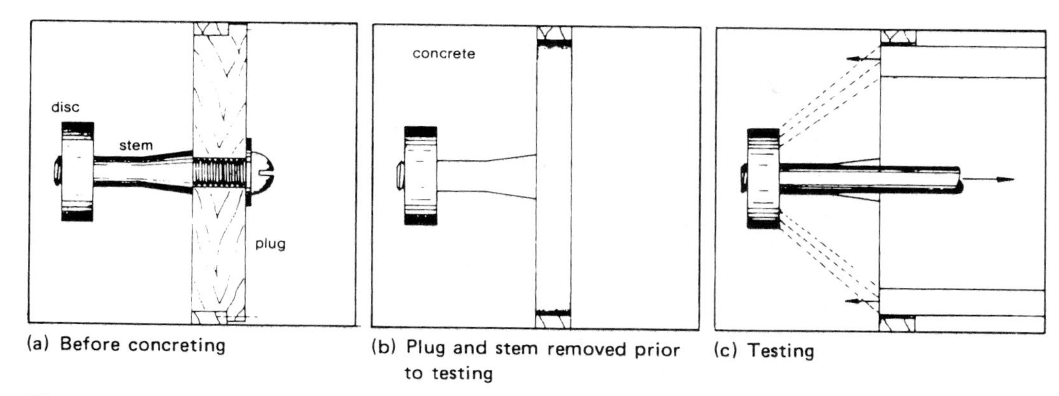

(a) Before concreting (b) Plug and stem removed prior to testing (c) Testing

Figure 6.3 *The principle of the LOK test*

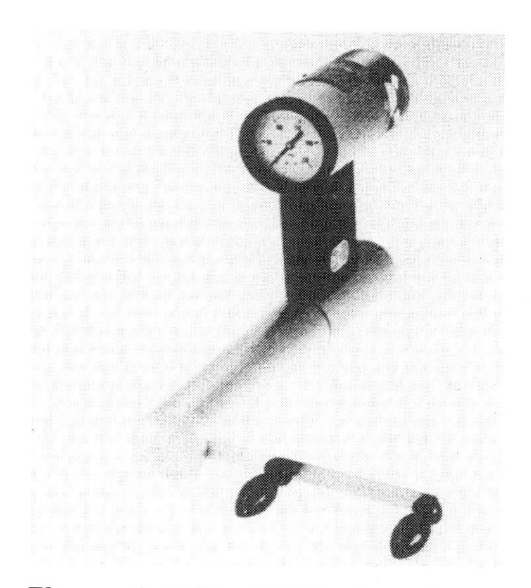

Figure 6.4 *The LOK test equipment*

Pull-out testing has been used in UK, North America, Scandinavia, the Middle East and the Far East. It has a major advantage over penetration tests and break-off tests in having a single correlation. Because the cover to the discs is only 25 mm, there is a chance of corrosion in the discs and surface blemishes if they remain in the concrete. Corrosion-resistant discs are also available.

6.6 BREAK-OFF TESTS

Figure 6.5 illustrates the procedure for the break-off (TNS) test[68]. At least five plastic sleeves are pressed into the fresh concrete. Prior to testing, the sleeves are removed leaving a cylinder of concrete which is fixed at its base. A force is applied via a special hydraulic ram to break off these cylinders. The average of the five results is taken as the break-off force. Keiller estimates[65] that, for a range of mature concretes, the 90% confidence limits are ± 8 N/mm^2. Data are not published on the confidence limits in young concrete.

(a) Placing plastic sleeves in the fresh concrete

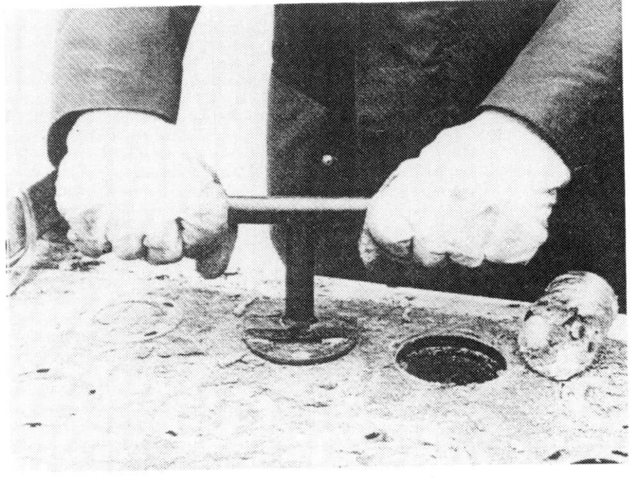

(b) Removing the plastic sleeve prior to testing

(c) The free-standing cylinder of concrete

(d) Testing

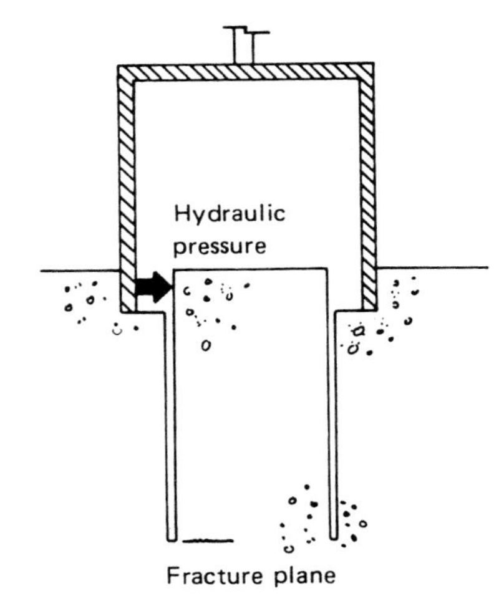

(e) The principle of the break-off test

Figure 6.5 *The break-off test*

6.7 MATURITY MEASUREMENTS

Maturities can be measured in several ways:

1. Recording the temperature of the section, say, every hour, then calculating the equivalent age at 20°C, using the activation energy equation (see Section 4.2) or, if appropriate, the Sadgrove equation. See Appendix D for an example.

2. Using a maturity meter (see Figure 6.6). A temperature sensing probe is pushed into the freshly compacted concrete, and the meter automatically calculates the maturity. The accuracy of the meter should be checked using cubes. Place the probe in one of a batch of freshly compacted cubes stored in one place, then test pairs of cubes at various ages. Compare the strength calculated from maturity to actual cube strength. If the scatter is reasonable, calculate the 90% confidence limits. Use the lower 90% confidence as the relationship betwen strength and maturity as this gives a 95% probability that the strength is greater than estimated. A more detailed description of how maturity can be used to control formwork striking times is given in Reference 51.

3. Using the COMA maturity probe (see Figure 6.7). This comprises a liquid-filled capillary tube fixed to a maturity scale, all encased in a glass container. The end of the capillary tube is broken off, so that the liquid evaporates at a rate dependent on temperature. The capillary tube and scale are then screwed back into their glass container, and the whole COMA probe is pushed into the freshly compacted concrete. Periodically, the maturity is checked (see Figure 6.7) until the desired maturity for removing the formwork is attained.

As the concrete strength is not being tested directly, it is important to be reasonably sure that the concrete is as specified. This can be done by taking control cubes and testing them prior to form removal. The maturity at testing should be calculated and the results checked against the reference strength/maturity relationship. Reference 51 describes how this relationship can be adjusted to reflect the day-to-day variations in concrete quality.

Figure 6.6 *A maturity meter (photograph by courtesy of Wexham Developments Ltd.)*

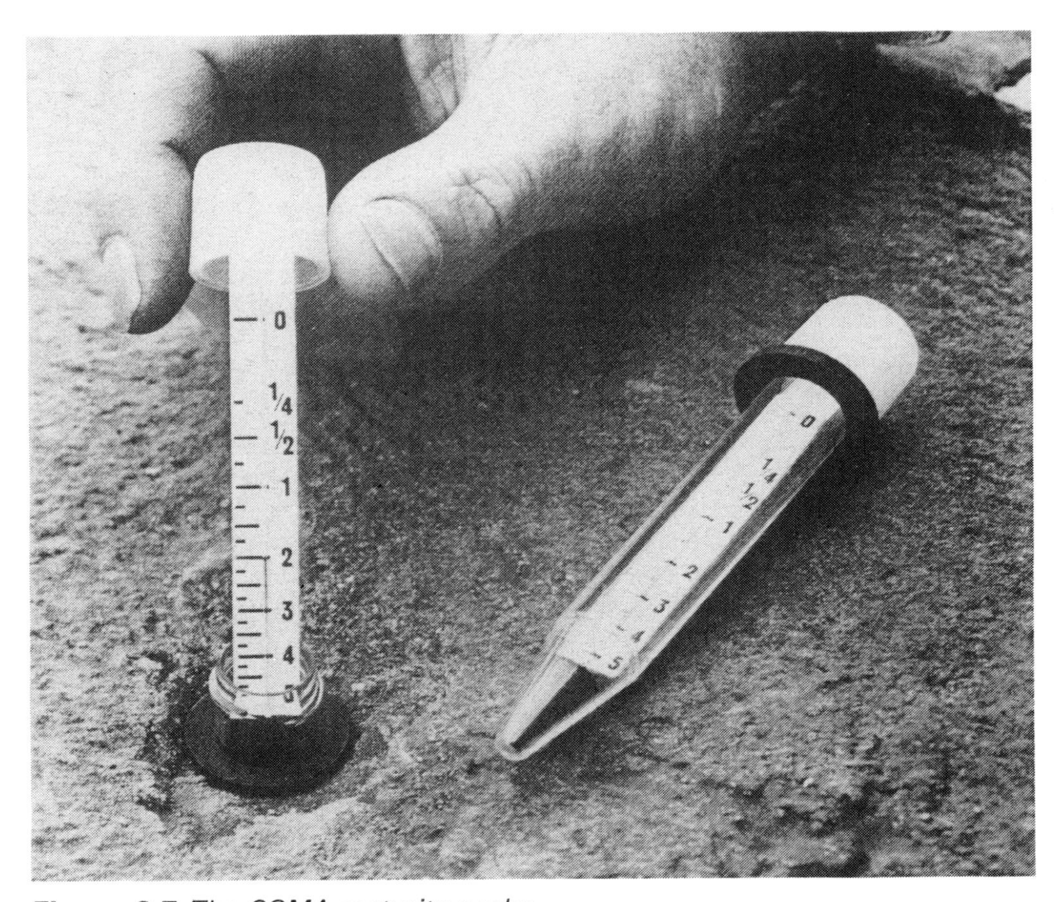

Figure 6.7 *The COMA maturity probe*

7 Conclusions

1. Research effort has managed to define, in terms of the required cube strength, most of the striking time criteria to an acceptable degree of accuracy. The main factors involved in the gain of strength of in-situ concrete are known. However, for a given grade of concrete, the rate of strength gain varies widely. This affects the striking times.

2. The key to striking times is the characteristic in-situ cube strength, but this cannot be directly measured. Indirect methods have to be used to assess the strength, and these all have their limitations. But when they are used with understanding and care, economical striking of formwork can be achieved without detriment to the structure.

3. There are a number of established methods for predicting the maturity and thus the strength of a hydrating concrete section. These all give adequate estimates of maturity provided job-specific data are used.

4. Where job-specific data are not available, predictive methods can be used to define a range of maturities over which the strength at striking needs to be achieved. The concrete producer then quotes for a range of mixes that cover this range and the actual mix selected will be based on the conditions on the day of placing.

5. Most methods of assessing striking times apply equally well to all concretes. However, techniques based on measuring maturity or tables of striking times may require checks on their applicability.

6. The most appropriate techniques to use when rapid construction is required are temperature-matched cubes, in-situ test methods, or, in some instances, cubes cured alongside. For more traditional construction or minor works, the use of the tables given in this report is an appropriate method.

References

1. FIELD, J
Les défauts de construction, l'étayage des planchers dans les bâtiments à multi-étages
(Building failures: floor support shoring in multi-storey construction).
Building Research and Practice (CIB) May/June 1974 7(3), **151 to 155.**

2. WEAVER, J
Temperature development in hydraulic concrete
PhD Thesis, University of London, 1971

3. HUNT, J.G.
The early age thermal cracking of concrete road slabs
PhD Thesis, University of London, 1970

4. SADGROVE, B.M.
The early development of strength in concrete
CIRIA Technical Note 12, July 1970

5. SADGROVE, B.M.
The strength and deflection of reinforced concrete beams loaded at early age
CIRIA Technical Note 31, October 1971

6. SAMUELSSON, P.
Necessary early strength on in-situ cast concrete
In: *Concrete at Early Ages* RILEM Int. Conf. Vol.1, Paris, 1982

7. SADGROVE, B.M.
Freezing of concrete at an early age
Cement and Concrete Association, Technical Report 42.503, 1974

8. HARRISON, T.A.
Mechanical damage to concrete by early removal of formwork
Cement and Concrete Association, Technical Report 42.505, 1975

9. HARRISON, T.A.
Formwork striking times - methods of assessment
CIRIA Report 73, 1987

10. WEAVER, J. and SADGROVE, B.M.
Striking times of formwork - tables of curing periods to achieve given strengths
CIRIA Report 36, October 1971

11. HARRISON, T.A.
Tables of minimum striking times for soffit and vertical formwork
CIRIA Report 67, October 1977

12. CONCRETE SOCIETY/ INSTITUTION OF STRUCTURAL ENGINEERS
Formwork: A guide to good practice
Concrete Society, 1986

13. BRITISH STANDARDS INSTITUTION
Testing concrete
Part 101: Method of sampling fresh concrete on site
Part 108: Method for making test cubes from fresh concrete
Part 111: Method of normal curing of test specimens (20°C method)
Part 116: Method for determination of compressive strength of concrete cubes
BS1881: Part 101:1983; Part 108:1983; Part 111:1983; Part 116:1983

14. BRITISH STANDARDS INSTITUTION
Structural use of concrete: Code of practice for design and construction
BS8110: Part 1:1985

15. DAVIS, S.G. and MARTIN, S.J.
The quality of concrete and its variation in structures
Cement and Concrete Association Technical Report 42.487, November 1973

16. BUNGEY, J.H.
Testing concrete in structures. A guide to equipment for testing concrete in structures
CIRIA TN 143, 1992

17. BRITISH STANDARDS INSTITUTION
Guide to assessment of concrete strength in existing structures
BS 6089: 1981

18. WILSON, R.
Short-term behaviour of reinforced concrete loaded at early ages
In: *Concrete at Early Ages* RILEM Int. Conf. Vol.1, Paris, 1982

19. HARRISON, T.A.
The application of accelerated curing to apartment formwork systems
Cement and Concrete Association Advisory Note 45.032, 1977

20. NIELSEN, K.E.C.
Loads on reinforced concrete floor slabs and their deformation during construction
Swedish Cement and Concrete Research Institute at the Royal Institute of Technology (Stockholm). Handlingar 15, 1952

21. GRUNDY, P. and KARAILA, A.
Construction loads on slabs with shored formwork in multi-storey buildings
Journal-American Concrete Institute (Detroit). December 1963 **34** (Title No. 60-73), **1729 to 1738**

22. BERESFORD, F.D.
An analytical examination of propped floors
Constructional Review November 1964 **37** (No. 11), **16 to 20**

23. BLAKEY, F.A. and BERESFORD, F.D.
Stripping of formwork for concrete in buildings in relation to structural design
Civil Engineering Transactions (Australia) October 1965 **CE7**(2), **92 to 96**

24. MAROSSZEKY, M.
Construction load imposed in multi-storey structures
Civil Engineering Transactions (Australia) April 1972 **CE12**(1), **91 to 93**

25. AGARWAL, R.K. and GARDNER, N.J.
Form and shore requirements for multistorey flat slab type buildings
Journal-American Concrete Institute (Detroit) November 1974 **45**
(Title No. 71-38), **559 to 569**

26. NOBLE, J.
Stop guessing at reshore load – measure them
Concrete Construction July 1975, **277 to 280**

27. DEPARTMENT OF TRANSPORT
Surface finishes for concrete
In: *Specification for Highway Works, Series 1700 Structural concrete*
Her Majesty's Stationery Office (London) 1991, **24**

28. POWERS, T.C. and BROWNYARD, T.L.
Studies of the physical properties of hardened Portland cement paste
Journal-American Concrete Institute (Detroit)
Part 1 Oct. 1946 **8**(2), **101 to 132**
Part 2 Nov. 1946 **8**(3), **246 to 336**

29. HARRISON, T.A.
Early-age thermal crack control in concrete
CIRIA Report 91 revised, 1993

30. BELLANDER, U.
Handling of concrete in winter
In: *ERMCO 1983: Concrete Technology Sessions W13B and W14B*
ERMCO, 1983

31. LI, A.I and KRYLOU, B.A.
Electrode heating of concrete
In: *RILEM recommendations for concreting in cold weather: Appendix 12*
Tech.
Res. Centre of Finland, 1988

32. SPOONER, D.C
BCA computer model for temperature rise prediction in fresh concrete
British Cement Asso. TDH 51062, undated but used in 1992

33. de SITTER, W.R and RAMLER, J.P.G.
The concrete hardening control system: CHCS
In: *Testing during concrete construction* RILEM. Edited by H.W. Reinhardt, pp. 224-242. Chapman and Hall, 1990

34. HANSON, P.F. and PEDERSEN, E.J.
Vinterstøbning af beton (in Danish)
Statens Byggeforskningsinstitut, 1982

35. JONASSON, J-E.
Slipform construction - calculations for assessing protection against early freezing
Swedish C&CA Report 4.84, 1984

36. BYFORS, J.
Performance concrete for more accurate and earlier form stripping during winter time
In: *ERMCO 1989 Proc."The Norway to Concrete"* The Norwegian Ready Mixed Conc. Asso., 1989

37. PITKÄNEN, P.
Prediction of temperature fields of massive concrete structures during hardening
Nordic Conc.Res. Pub. No. 3, 1984, **183 to 190**

38. ACKER, P.
Thermal effects in concrete during manufacture and applications to engineering structures (in French with an English summary)
Annales de L 'Institute Technique du Bâtiment et des Travaux Publics No. 442, Feb. 1986, **61 to 80**

39. CUR
Cooling of concrete (in Dutch with English summary)
CUR Report 128, 1987

40. REKNES, K.
Computer calculations of temperature and strength development of the hardening concrete (PhD thesis in Norwegian)
Norwegian Inst. of Tech., NTH1990:77 Parts1&2, 1990

41. ULLA KJÆR
Computer Interactive Maturity System (CIMS)
Nordic Concrete Research, 1987 **131 to 140**

42. DANSK TEKNOLOGISK INSTITUT
Some commonly asked questions about CIMS
Dansk Teknologisk Institut (supplier of equipment and software), 1991

43. ASTM
Standard practice for estimating concrete strength by the maturity method
ASTM C1074-87(90-edit. changes)

44. HANSEN, P. F. and PEDERSEN, E.J.
Curing of concrete structures
In: *CEB Design Guide "Durable Concrete Structures"*, CEB Bull. No.182, Lausanne, June 1989

45. CARINO, N.J. and TANK, R.C.
Maturity functions of concrete made with various cements and admixtures
ACI Mat. J.,Vol.89, No.2, March-April 1992

46. DE VRIES, P.
Maturity of concrete according to De Vries
Note distributed to CEN TC104/SC1/TG7. Doc.12,1992

47. HANSEN, P. F. and PEDERSEN, E.J.
Maleinstrument til kontrol af betons haerdning (Maturity computer for controlled curing and hardening of concrete)
Nordisk Betong (J. Nordic Concrete Fed.) 1977 No. 1, **21 to 26**

48. COMMISSION 42-CEA
Properties of set concrete at early ages - State of the art report
Matériaux et Constructions (RILEM) Nov/Dec 1981 **14**(No. 84)

49. BRESSON, J.
La prévision des résistances des produits en béton
In: *Concrete at Early Ages* RILEM Int. Conf. Vol.1, Paris, April 1982

50. SADGROVE, B.M.
Prediction of strength development in concrete structures
In: *54th Annual meeting of the Transportation Research Board*
Washington DC, Jan. 1975

51. NICKLINSON, A.J
A practical method for assessing the early in-situ strength of concrete
Institute of Conc. Tech. ACT Project, 1991

52. WIMPENNY, D., ELLIS, C., REEVES,C.M. and HIGGINS, D.D.
The development of strength and elastic properties in slag cement concretes under low temperature curing conditions.
In: *Proc. Int. Conf. on blended cements, Trondheim, 1989* ACI SP114, Volume 2 Ed. V M Malhotra 1989 **1283 to 1306**

53. DHIR, R.K., MUNDAY, J.G.L. and ONG, L.T.
Investigations of the engineering properties of OPC/pulverized-fuel ash concrete: strength development and maturity
In: *Proc. Instn. Civ. Engrs., Part 2*, June 1984 **239 to 254**

54. MAGNE MAAGE
Strength and heat development in concrete: Influence of fly ash and condensed silica fume
In: *Fly ash, silica fume, slag and natural pozzolans in concrete* ACI SP.91, Vol. 2, 1986 **923 to 940**

55. HARRISON, T.A.
Early-age temperature rises in concrete sections with reference to BS 5337: 1976
Cement and Concrete Association, ITN5, 1978

56. HARRISON, T.A. and SPOONER, D.C.
The properties and use of concretes made with composite cements
Cement and Concrete Association, Interim Technical Note 10, Nov. 1986

57. CONCRETE SOCIETY
The use of GGBS and PFA in concrete
Concrete Society Technical Report No. 40, 1991

58. LAWRENCE, C.D., DALZIEL, J.A.and HOBBS, D.W.
Sulphate attack arising from delayed ettringite formation
British Cement Association ITN 12, 1990

59. CANNON, R.P.
Measurement of the in-situ strength and temperature development of concretes containing Portland and Portland blastfurnace cements
Silicates Industriels 1982-7/8, **183 to 187**

60. BLAKEY, H.
Temperature matching curing bath - an aid to earlier formwork striking
Concrete May 1976 **10**(10), **25 and 26**

61. BRITISH STANDARDS INSTITUTION
Method for temperature-matched curing of concrete specimens
BSI DD 92: 1984

62. BUNGEY, J.H.
Testing by penetration resistance
Concrete January 1981 **15**(1), **30 to 32**

63. SWAMY, R.N. and AL-HAMED, A.H.M.S.
Evaluation of the Windsor Probe test to assess in-situ concrete strength
In: *Proc. Instn. Civ. Engr.* June 1984 **77**(Part 2), **167 to 194**

64. KEILLER, A.P.
A preliminary investigation of test methods for the assessment of strength of in-situ concrete
Cement and Concrete Association Technical Report 551, 1982

65. KRENCHEL, H. and PETERSEN, C.G.
In-situ pull-out testing with LOK test: Ten years experience
In: *In-situ/Non-destructive Testing of Concrete,* Int. Conf., Ottawa, Canada, 1984

66. BICKLEY, J.A.
The variability of pullout tests and in-place concrete strength
Concrete International (Am. Concr. Inst., Detroit) April 1982 **4**(4), **44 to 51**

67. BICKLEY, J.A.
Achieving safety and economy in high rise concrete structures through the use of in-place testing
In: *3rd Int. Conf. on Tall Buildings,* Chicago, 1986

68. JOHANSEN, R.
In-situ strength evaluation of concrete - the 'break-off' method
Concrete International (Am. Concr. Inst. Detroit) September 1979 **1**(9), **45 to 81**

69. BRITISH STANDARDS INSTITUTION
Wind loads
CP3: Chapter V: Part 2: 1972

Appendix A: Selection of concrete strength required to withstand a known wind loading on a reinforced concrete wall or column

A.1 INTRODUCTION

Because of the low strengths recommended as suitable for striking of vertical formwork, wind loading on a free-standing wall may be a limiting factor.

Figures A.1 to A.3 apply to vertically-reinforced walls where the concrete contains normal weight aggregate. Plain walls should be treated as gravity structures, and propping might be necessary after the formwork is struck.

Using Figure A.3, find the intersection of the height of lift and the thickness of the wall. From the intersection point, check if the concrete strength is critical. If it could affect the striking time, obtain the probable maximum wind speed in the next 24 h from the meteorological office and recheck, using the appropriate chart.

If the concrete strength is still critical, there are the alternatives of leaving the formwork in place until the necessary strength is achieved, or of striking and re-propping.

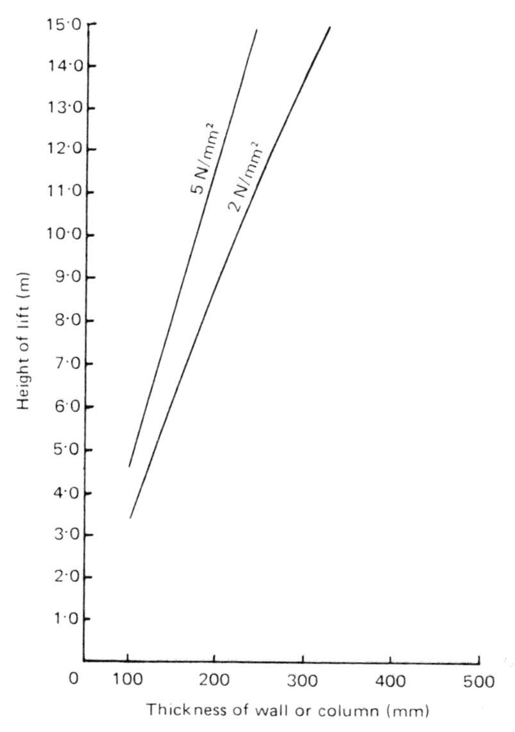

Figure A.1 *Cube strength required to withstand wind speeds up to 10 m/s(36 km/h)*

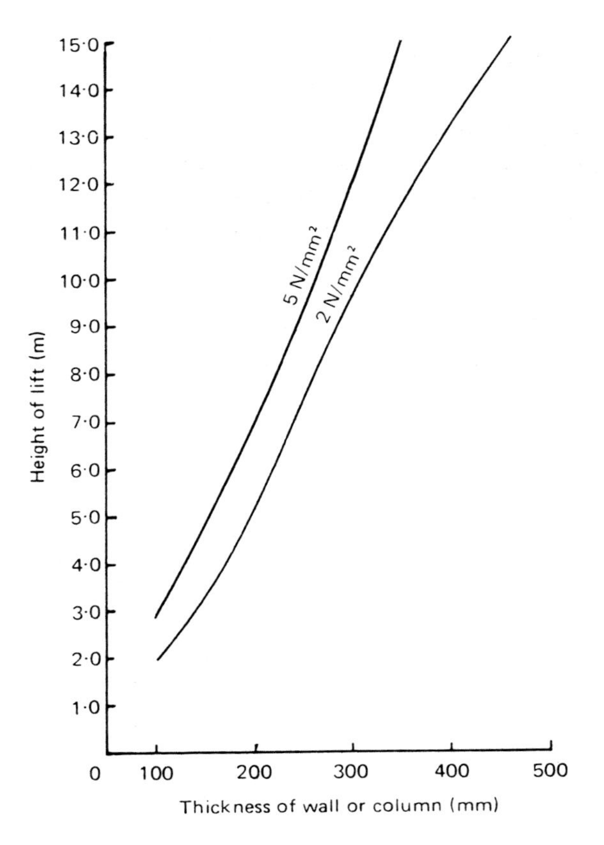

Figure A.2 *Cube strength required to withstand wind speeds up to 15 m/s(54 km/h)*

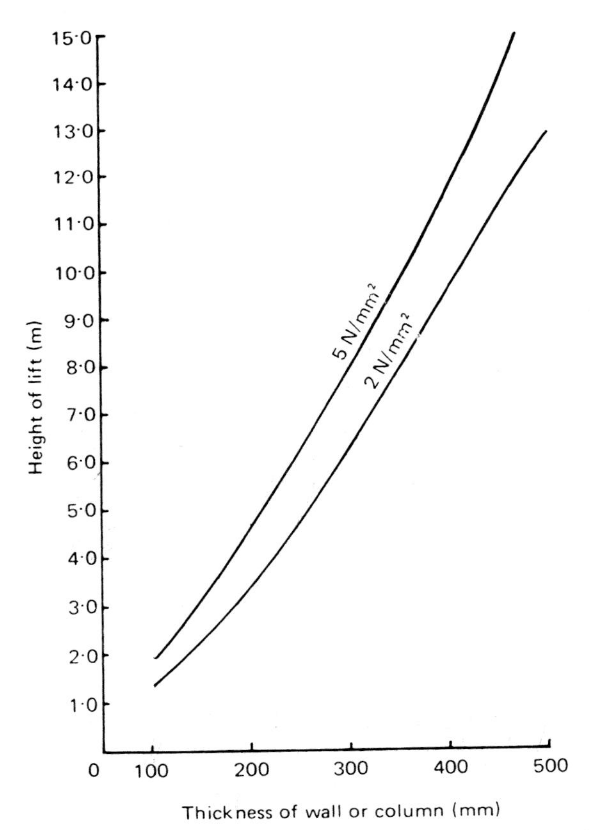

Figure A.3 *Cube strength required to withstand windspeeds up to 20 m/s (72 km/h)*

A.2 DERIVATION OF CHARTS

The wall is taken to be a long free-standing reinforced concrete wall. Consider a 1-m length of wall of height of lift, L. By inspection of the self-weight and bending moment diagrams in Figure A.4, the critical section is at AA, the construction joint. The forces acting at this section are the self-weight of the wall and the bending forces created by the wind load.

There are two possible failure mechanisms: by crushing of the concrete, or by insufficient anchorage bond from the starter bars.

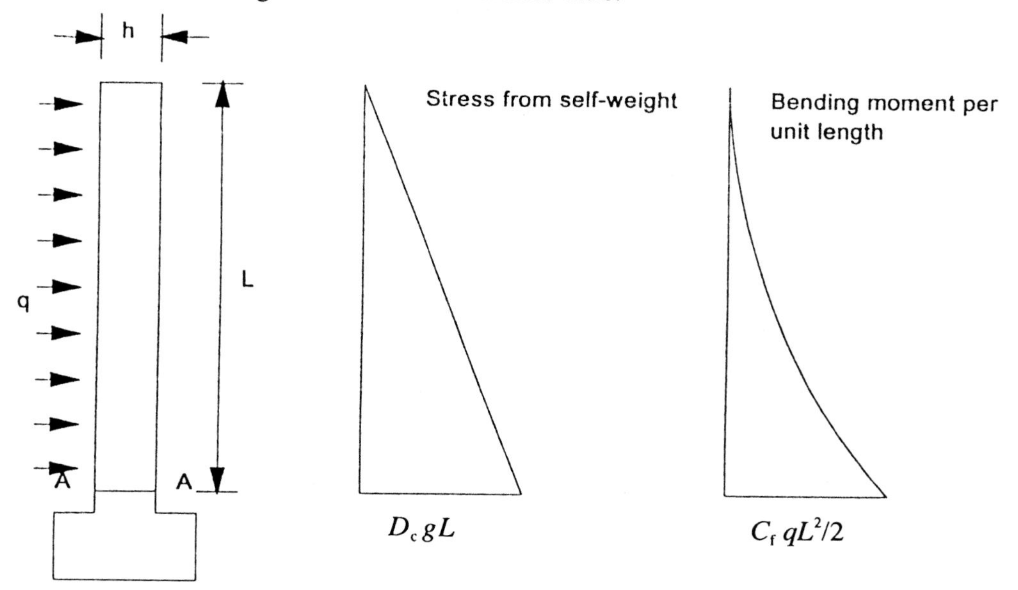

Figure A.4 *Wind loads on walls*

A.2.1 Crushing of the concrete

Self-weight

Stress from self-weight = $9.81 \times 10^{-6} D_c L$ N/mm^2
Putting concrete density, $D_c = 2330$ kg/m^3
Stress from self-weight = $0.0229 L$ N/mm^2

As the compressive strength under axial load is 0.67 times the cube strength, the characteristic in-situ cube strength required

$$= \frac{0.0229}{0.67} L$$

$= 0.0341 L$ N/mm^2

Hence, characteristic strength required from cubes of equal maturity to the wall is

$$f_l = \gamma_{mc} \times 0.0341 L$$

Putting $\gamma_{mc} = 1.5$ [A.1]

$$f_l = 0.0512 L \text{ N/mm}^2$$

Wind force

Horizontal force on a 1m length of wall $= C_f qL \times 10^6$ N

From Tables 4 and 20 of CP 3: Chapter V: Part 2: 1972[69]

$q = 0.613\ V_s^2 \times 10^{-6}$ N/mm^2

and $C_f = 2.0$

Hence moment at AA,

$$M_w = \frac{C_f\, qL^2}{2}$$

$$= 613\ V_s^2 L^2 \text{ N.mm} \qquad \text{[A.2]}$$

The characteristic cube strength, f_2, required to resist this moment is given by Equation [3.1]. This takes into account the equivalent cube factor and γ_{mc}. Thus

$$M_u = 0.15 f_2 b d^2$$

For a 1m length of wall

$$M_u = 150 f_2 d^2 \qquad \text{[A.3]}$$

In this case, M_u is equal to M_w and therefore combining Equations [A.2] and [A.3] and rearranging

$$f_2 = 4.09 \frac{V_s^2}{d^2} L^2 \text{ N/mm}^2 \qquad \text{[A.4]}$$

Combined stresses

The characteristic cube strength required to resist direct and bending stress

$$f_{cu} = f_1 + f_2$$

Substituting from Equations [A.1] and [A.4]

$$4.09 \frac{V_s^2}{d^2} L^2 + 0.0512L - f_{cu} = 0 \qquad \text{[A.5]}$$

Values of V_s , and f_{cu} are selected and Equation [A.5] solved for L.

A.2.2 Check on anchorage bond failure

Assume that the concrete does not crush and that the wall tends to rotate about its extreme edge.

Consider a 1m length of wall

The moment on the wall from wind loading, M_w, equals 613 $V_s^2 L^2$ N.mm

This is resisted by a self-weight moment of $22.9 \dfrac{h^2}{2} L = 11.5\, h^2 L$ N.mm

and by the anchorage bond moment of $\dfrac{1000d}{s_b}(25\varnothing + 150)\, \pi \varnothing f_{ba}$ N.mm

Equating these moments

$$613\, V_s^2 L^2 - 11.5\, h^2 L - \frac{1000d}{s_b}(25\varnothing + 150)\, \pi \varnothing f_{ba} = 0 \qquad [A.6]$$

By assuming the minimum percentage of steel, distributed in large diameter bars at wide spacings, Equation [A.6] was solved for the maximum height of lift.

A.2.3 Derivation of figures

For a given wall thickness, the lower of the two heights of lift obtained from Equations [A.5] and [A.6] was taken in deriving Figures A.1, A.2 and A.3.

Appendix B: The application of the Sadgrove equation to cements containing ggbs

The following analysis uses data from reference 52. The data for 20°C curing are plotted as a solid line and the data for curing at other temperatures have been converted to equivalent ages at 20°C and plotted as points. If the point lies on or above the solid line, it indicates that the Sadgrove equation is accurate or safe. If the points are significantly below the line, the Sadgrove equation is not safe.

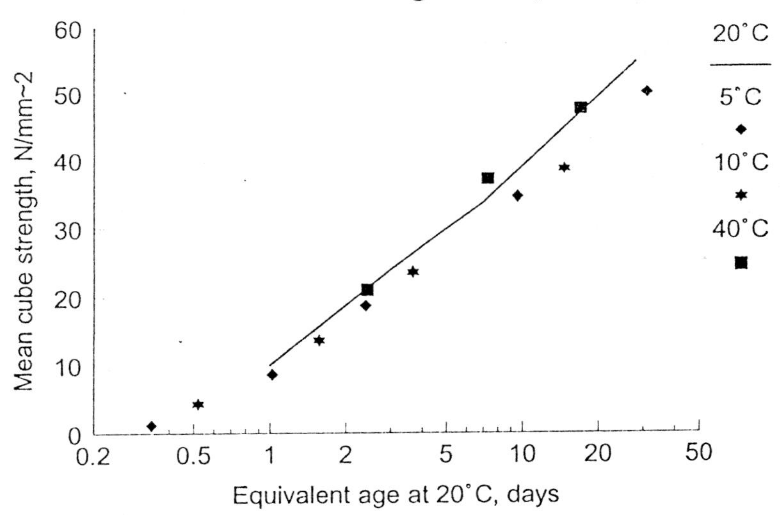

Figure B.1 *Mix A with 40% ggbs 1*

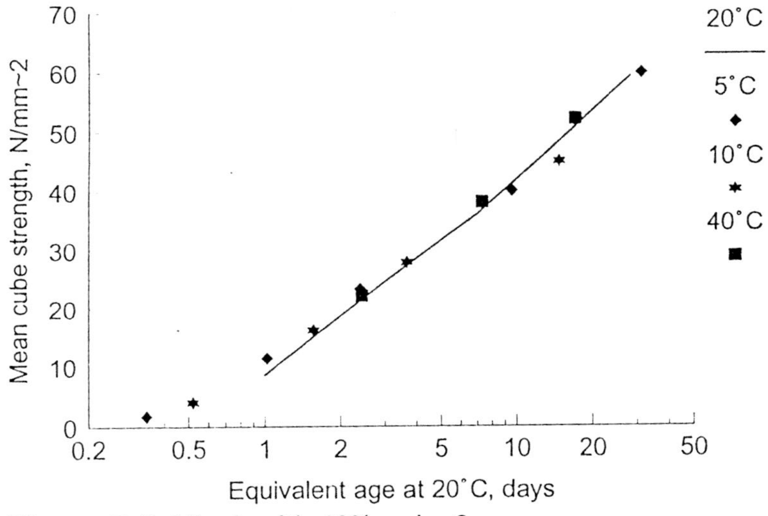

Figure B.2 *Mix A with 40% ggbs 2*

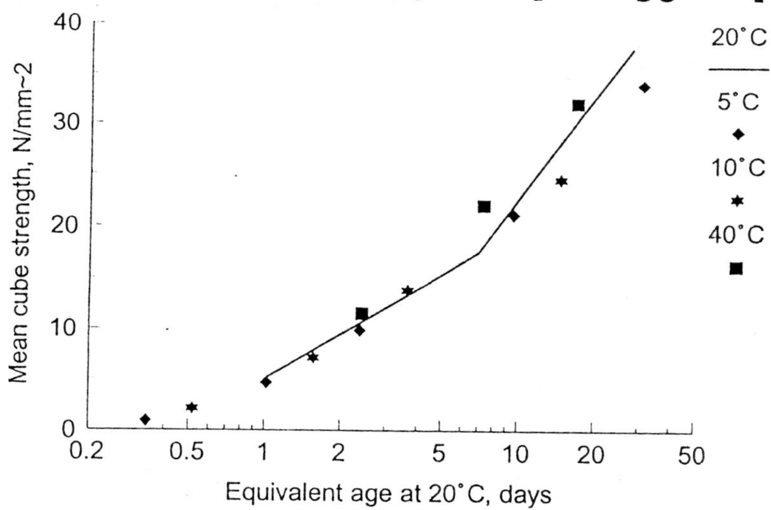

Figure B.3 *Mix B with 40% ggbs 1*

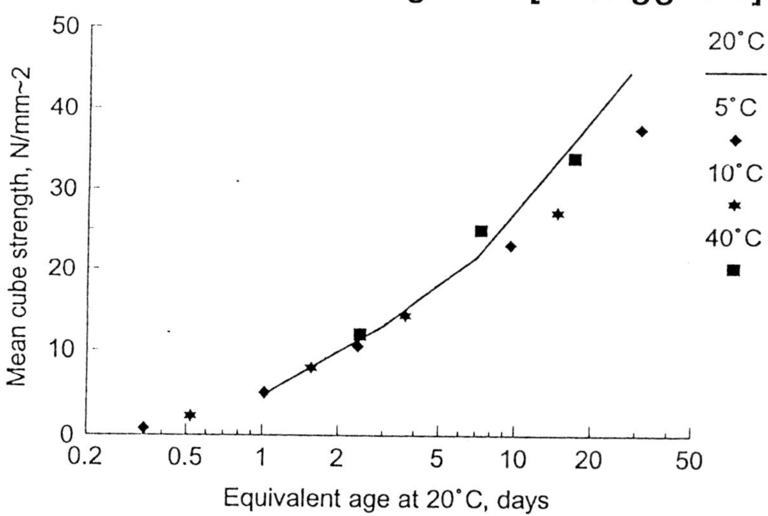

Figure B.4 *Mix B with 40% ggbs 2*

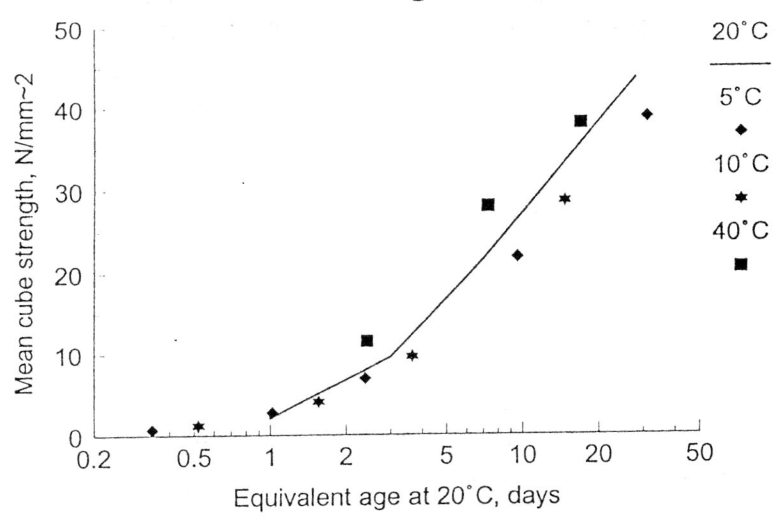

Figure B.5 *Mix A with 70% ggbs 1*

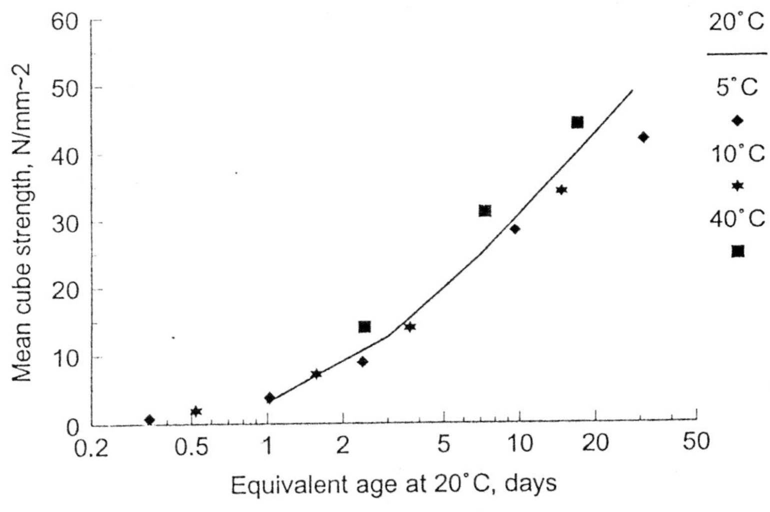

Figure B.6 *Mix A with 70% ggbs 2*

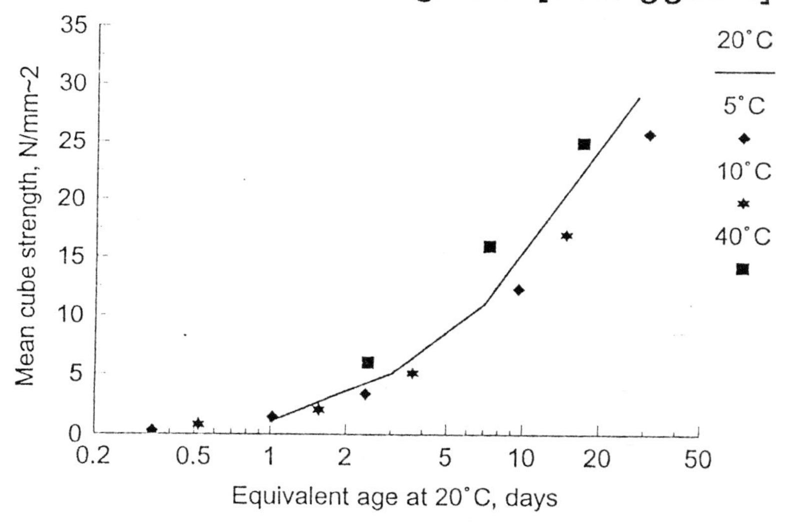

Figure B.7 *Mix B with 70% ggbs 1*

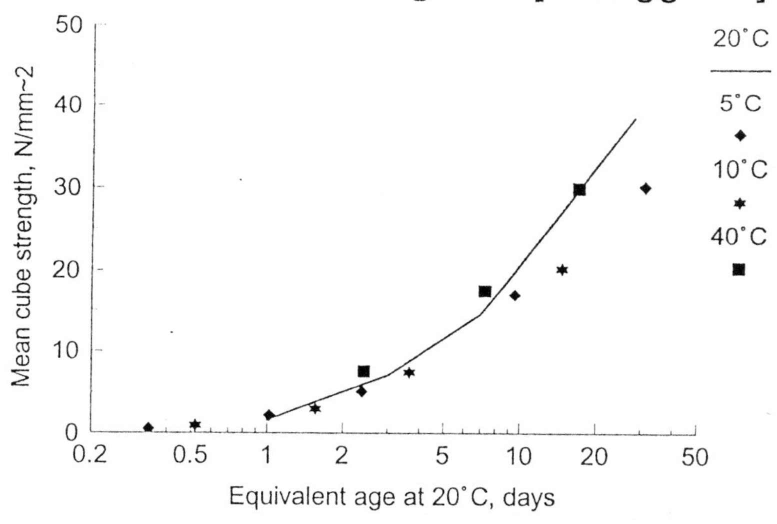

Figure B.8 *Mix B with 70% ggbs 2*

Appendix C: The application of the Sadgrove equation to cements containing pfa

The following analysis uses data from Table 5 of reference 53. The data for 20°C curing are plotted as a solid line and the data for curing at other temperatures have been converted to equivalent ages at 20°C and plotted as points. If the point lies on or above the solid line, it indicates that the Sadgrove equation is accurate or safe. If the points are significantly below the line, the Sadgrove equation is not safe.

Figures C.1 to C.4 show that the Sadgrove equation is reasonable in the temperature range 5 to 30°C. This conclusion is based on the mean strengths obtained from one Portland cement to BS12 combined with a range of pfas of different qualities.

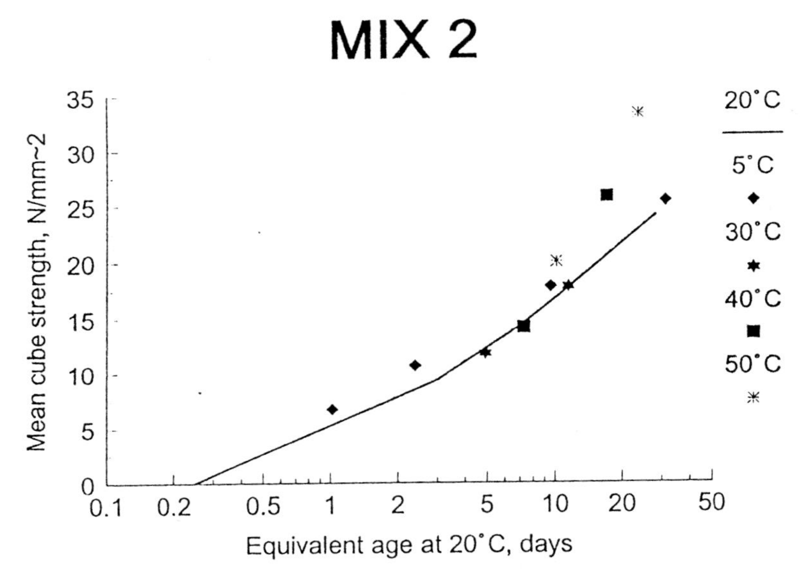

Figure C.1 *Mix M2*

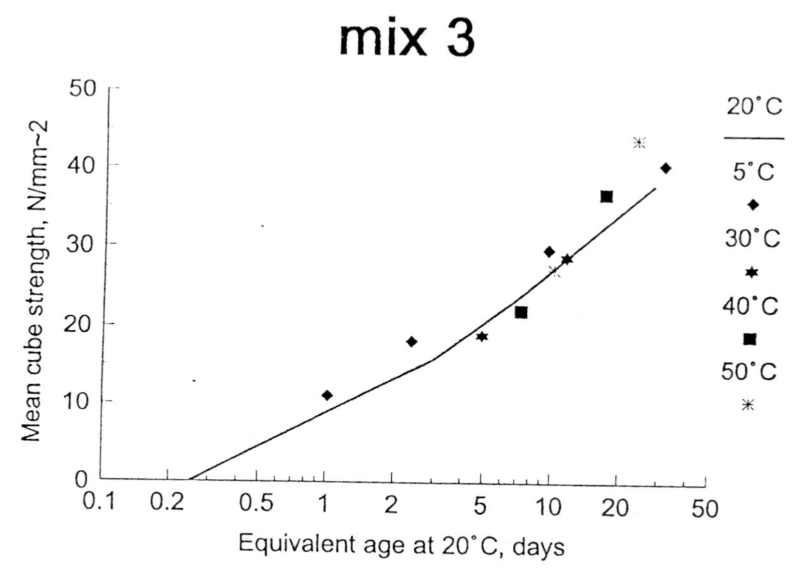

Figure C.2 *Mix M3*

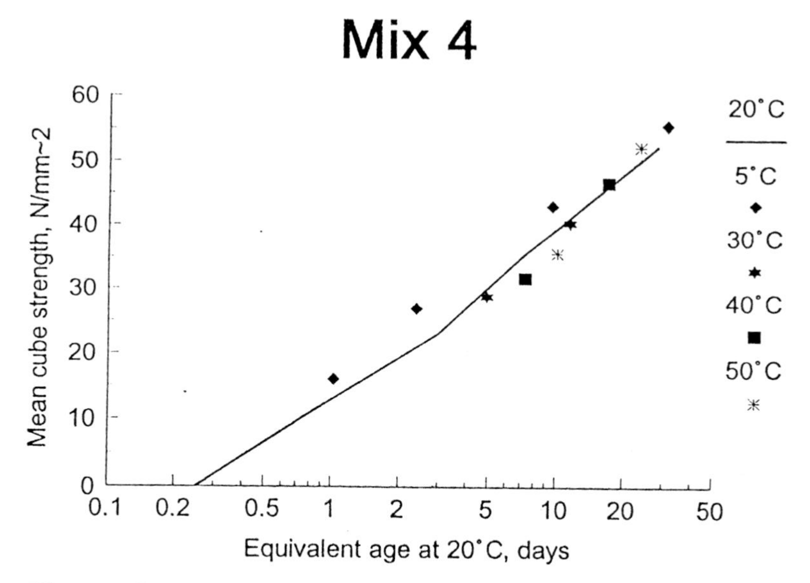

Figure C.3 *Mix M4*

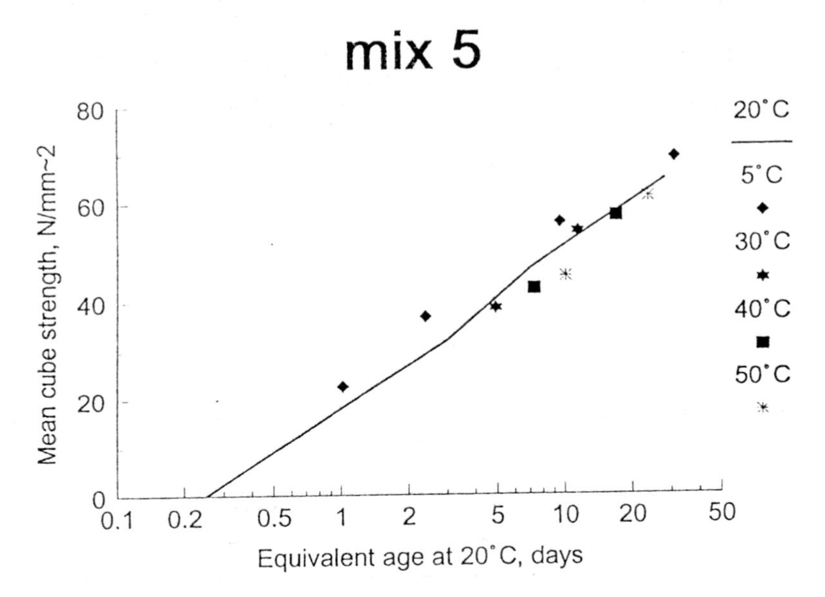

Figure C.4 *Mix M5*

Appendix D: Example of a hand calculation of maturity using the Sadgrove equation (Section 4.2)

$$\textit{Equivalent age at } 20°C = \Sigma\left(\frac{\theta+16}{36}\right)^2 \Delta t$$

Time from casting hrs	Conc. temp. °C	Δt hrs	Av. conc. temp. in Δt °C	$k = \left(\frac{\theta+16}{36}\right)^2$	$k\Delta t$ hrs	$\Sigma k\Delta t$ hrs
0	7					
		2	6.5	0.391	0.782	
2	6					0.78
		2	7	0.408	0.816	
4	8					1.78
		2	9	0.482	0.964	
6	10					2.56
		2	10.5	0.542	1.084	
8	11					3.64
		2	11	0.563	1.125	
10	11					4.77
		2	11.5	0.584	1.167	
12	12					5.94
		2	11.5	0.584	1.167	
14	11					7.10
		2	11	0.563	1.125	
16	11					8.23
		2	10.5	0.542	1.084	
18	10					9.31
		2	9.5	0.502	1.003	
20	9					10.32
		2	9	0.482	0.965	
22	9					11.28
		2	8.5	0.463	0.926	
24	8					12.21

After a real time of 24 hours the maturity of the section was equivalent to 12.2 hours at 20°C.